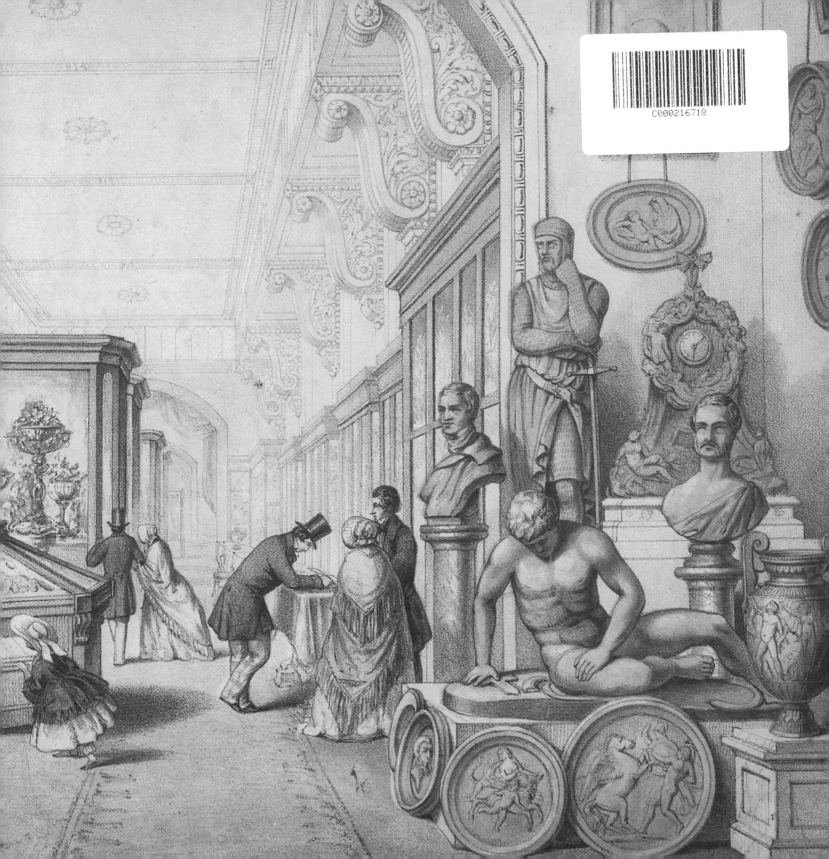

C000216718

Invention & Design
Elkington of Birmingham

Jonathan Berg

Birmingham Picture Library 2021

First published in 2021 by Birmingham Picture Library

14 St Bernard's Road, Olton

Solihull, B92 7BB

Tel: 0121 765 4114

Facebook: @postivelybrum

Instagram: @positivelybirminghamtours

Twitter: @postivelybrum

Email: info@positivelybirmingham.co.uk

www.positivelybirmingham.co.uk

© Photos and text, Jonathan Berg, 2021

All rights reserved. No part of this publication may be reproduced, stored in a retrieval system or transmitted in any form or by any means, electronic, mechanical, photocopying, recording or otherwise without the prior permission of the publishers.

A CIP catalogue record for this book is available from the British Library.

ISBN 978 0 9523179 9 9

Designed and edited by John Williams

Printed by: Gutenberg Press, Malta

Front cover
A range of Elkington products photographed outside the Whitmore Warehouse on the site of the Elkington Newhall Street factory.

Back cover
Elkington teapot (1874), milk jug (1874) and coffee pot (1857) photographed by Lock No. 1 of the Birmingham & Fazeley Canal which ran through the Elkington factory.

Title page
Woodbrooke, George Richards Elkington's family home reflected in a fruit bowl by Elkington (1965, pattern 38385) in an Art Deco inspired sunburst shape.

Endpapers
Detail of an engraving of the Elkington showroom at the Newhall Street factory

Contents

Preface

This book is not a standard history of the firm of Elkington, nor is it a catalogue of their products. It is instead a very personal work which combines three of my main interests: the city of Birmingham, photography and, more recently, collecting the electroplated products of Elkington & Co.

I came to Birmingham in 1978 from Bristol. I was fascinated by the city, and especially by the way that living industrial history could be found around every corner. Cycling through Sparkbrook and Small Heath to the hospital where I worked, I could see sparks flying as molten metal was poured at a brass foundry – in a process which seemed little changed since Victorian times – as well as the enormous site of the recently closed BSA factory.

My interest grew and I read about the Georgian giants of industry such as Boulton, Watt and Murdoch, the phenomenal growth of Victorian Birmingham, and the Civic Gospel and Municipal Revolution movements which ensured the city could cope with that growth. The Jewellery Quarter held a particular fascination – we bought our wedding rings there and, on rainy Sunday afternoons, would visit the Industrial Museum on the site of the once huge Elkington factory.

Jonathan Berg

In the 1990s, I began a photographic mission to explore the city. It resulted in five editions of *Positively Birmingham* – one citizen exploring the modern city in text and images. In 2019, I also began to collect Elkington products as I researched this book. While the company made some remarkable and elaborate items – which today would be extremely expensive to purchase – most of its wares were much more modest and are within easy reach of any collector. With a few exceptions, the items illustrated here were bought for £20 or less.

While working on my previous books, I had been surprised to find that the achievements of the Elkingtons were so little known – their story is one which has much to say about the inventiveness and cross-fertilisation of ideas which have powered Birmingham's success. This book sets out to remedy that, to put Elkington and its products in their Birmingham context, and to reveal the simple beauty of these everyday items.

I hope you enjoy learning about Elkington as much as I have enjoyed telling their story.

Jonathan Berg
November 2021

Foreword

Today, Birmingham's Jewellery Quarter seems a very different place from how it was in the era described in this book. It is a 'gentrified' conservation area in which the inhabitants of modern executive flats live amongst fine surviving Victorian buildings in what has been described as an 'urban village'. Located just outside the city centre it is home to a thriving hospitality industry with many highly acclaimed restaurants and bars. And naturally many of the visitors who come to the 'The Quarter' today are still attracted by its jewellery retailers, workshops and manufacturers.

The story told in this book brings to life the entrepreneurial way in which George and Henry Elkington, along with their associates, developed their business. Today we would call it 'networking', with the two cousins using all their skills and contacts to advance their dream. They brought together leaders in other fields from design, patenting and innovative manufacturing, right through to marketing and promotion. They harnessed newly invented processes and technologies to manufacture beautiful items which were sold around the world. The Elkington story is an important part of the history of the Jewellery Quarter, where many leading jewellery and giftware manufacturers still thrive today, but it also demonstrates more generally how creating a hub of industries at the forefront of their technologies can bring with it huge success.

This book provides a succinct background to an important time for Birmingham and in particular for the Jewellery Quarter. It describes the early development of processes such as gilding, japanning and electroplating and how they were brought into full scale manufacturing. It is in interesting to read how the Elkington business supplied bespoke products to cruise liners, hotels and leading retailers.

Today, manufacturing in Birmingham, and the wider West Midlands, continues along the lines established in the era of Elkington. With thousands of engineering companies, this is still the workshop of the world. As in the Elkingtons' time, new technologies are still readily adopted, offering opportunities for varied production techniques. This remains a part of the country where it is possible to find a complete manufacturing supply chain around the corner – including design, raw materials, manufacturing, marketing, assembly and of course, most importantly, electroplating.

Henrik Skouby
Managing Director E.C. Williams
Spencer Street, Birmingham Jewellery Quarter

Henrik Skouby

Acknowledgements

Thanks should first go to my family, especially to Barbara for her practical support, despite the rather daunting prospect of seeing the house once again filled with boxes of newly-printed books! From her nursing home in Bristol, my mother-in-law Audrey has spurred on the project, regularly enquiring when she would see the finished book, while brother-in-law Barry has helped enthusiastically with checking the Elkington family history.

The support and enthusiasm of Alistair Grant from the University of Sussex and Angus Patterson, Senior Curator of Metalwork at the Victoria and Albert Museum, has been invaluable and most welcome, coming at just the right time for a project which has faced many lockdown-related issues. The help of Paul Taylor and colleagues at the Library of Birmingham is gratefully acknowledged, especially for allowing photography of the Elkington pattern books, and thanks are due to British Silverware for permission to reproduce these. Thanks must also go to Catherine Yates at the Local History Centre at Walsall Central Library and Archives and to Birmingham Museums Trust.

I am very grateful to Peter Chinn and Marc Harbourne-Bessant at the Woodbrooke Quaker Study Centre for help with location photography in the grounds of the former home of George Elkington, and to the Revd Hazel White, Vicar of St Mary's Selly Oak and the congregation of the Wednesday morning service for their help with photographs of the church. Thanks also to Neil Handley, Museum Curator at The College of Optometrists for allowing me to photograph spectacles from their collection, and to the Whitmore Collection for allowing photography in Newhall Square. I am also grateful to Laurence Butler at Thinktank, Birmingham Science Museum, and the Victoria and Albert Museum for allowing me to take photographs within their respective buildings.

I would also like to thank Ben McFarlane at J. Hudson & Co. for letting me photograph their Barr Street works, and Henrik Skouby at E.C. Williams for permission to photograph inside their Spencer Street factory – and of course for agreeing to write the Foreword.

A huge thank you to John Williams, who first edited the text into six flowing chapters, then designed the book you see before you. We have worked together now for over thirty years producing printed materials of all descriptions. We understand each other's strengths and weaknesses, and just like the story we tell here, that is so much the 'Birmingham way' of taking a project forward at a fast pace to a successful conclusion.

Finally, thanks to everyone who has come on the Sunday afternoon Positively Birmingham walking tour to the Jewellery Quarter, which has increasingly explored the Elkington story as this book has developed.

▶ ▼ Salt and Pepper (c.1947, pattern 25662). These two-piece salt and pepper pots, designed to be robust enough for commercial use, are photographed at a canal lock near the Elkington factory. Below the same design can be seen in an Elkington catalogue of the 1950s.

Introduction

The achievements of George and Henry Elkington and of Elkington & Co., the company they founded, were remarkable. They were among the very first to harness the commercial potential of electricity. They pioneered not just one but a series of revolutionary industrial techniques – processes which completely changed the way that things were made, and which continue to be essential for modern manufacturing. In addition, one of the associates they nurtured went on to manufacture the earliest form of plastic. On the basis of these achievements, and with a strong emphasis on the importance of good design, they built a company with an extraordinary range and volume of output. For over a century they produced not just high-end artistic products, but also everyday wares which were familiar in households up and down the land.

The success of the Elkington & Co. did not come out of the blue, but owed much to the way the manufacturers of Birmingham went about their business. This was a place where you could come with an idea and take it forward. There was a freedom to act in Birmingham, but it was also a hard-nosed business environment in which you had to be at the top of your game to succeed. This was a place where innovators of their day could share ideas – but also where innovation could give that essential competitive edge over others. The entrepreneurs of the Georgian age such as Baskerville, Boulton and Watt had already shown how successful this model could be, and the Elkingtons were among those who continued this spirit into the Victorian era.

It was to this place that James Elkington came from rural Warwickshire, marrying into the Richards family of 'toy' makers – producers of the small metal items for which Birmingham was then known. Living in a fine Georgian square, their son George grew up with the excitement of manufacturing all around. He learnt his trade from his uncles and saw for himself both the opportunities and the pressures brought about by an unprecedented rise in demand for Birmingham products, including the dangerous pollution it caused.

George was a natural inventor, early on patenting designs for improved spectacle frames. By the late 1830s, he and his younger cousin Henry were working on a range of innovations to take advantage of the latest scientific ideas, first patenting an 'immersion gilding' process which brought not only good profits, but also real benefits in reducing health risks, before developing their most important innovations. The first of these was electroplating – coating items with a thin layer of precious metal using electricity. The second was electrotyping – using electricity to form a solid metal object within a mould.

An astute choice of associates was key to developing their ideas and bringing their products to market. These included surgeon turned inventor John Wright, industrialist Josiah Mason, who was able to bring his experience as the world's largest pen nib manufacturer to grow the Elkington business, as well as Alexander Parkes, whose work for Elkington was the foundation for his invention of the first commercial plastic.

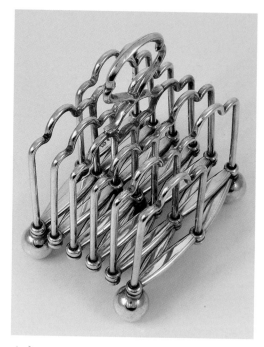

▲ ▶ Expanding rack (1859). One of Elkington's most ingenious designs, this folding rack is suitable for use both as a toast rack or as a letter rack. It is made up from 33 separate metal components with 13 brazing points and 19 hinged joints.

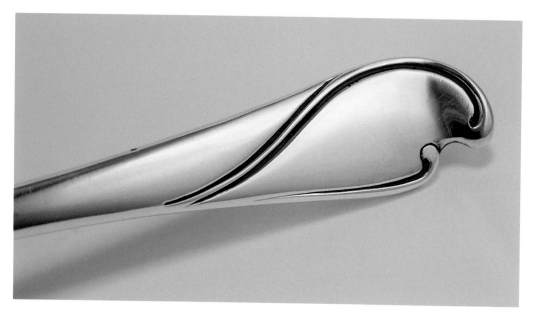

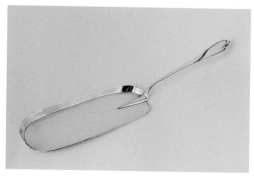

◀ ▲ Crumb tray (1886, pattern 46065). The elegant design of this handle typifies the simple beauty of many of Elkington's household wares and has a modernity which belies its age.

Elkington also worked with world-renowned designers and artists to produce a range of exclusive artistic pieces. This led to the firm's most famous collaboration – an arrangement with the Victoria and Albert Museum to make copies of famous artworks from collections around Europe which has been eloquently described by Alistair Grant and Angus Patterson in their book *The Museum and the Factory*.

This book focusses on another side of the Elkington factory output. When Josiah Mason joined the company in 1842, his good business sense pointed to the production of tableware and other mass-produced household items as the most profitable market. This 'flatware' and other small decorative and utility items were produced for the public on a huge scale. The growing service industry sector with its shipping lines, hotels and restaurants also became an important market for the company.

As well as recounting the story of the company, this book features Elkington products that anyone can purchase today – for example from an internet auction – for just a few pounds. These may be far simpler and cheaper than Elkington's most famous productions, but they are nevertheless often beautiful objects in their own right. To make it a little more fun, some of these items have been photographed on the site of the original Elkington factory in Newhall Street, in the neighbouring Jewellery Quarter and at Woodbrooke, George Elkington's former home.

Pleasingly, you can still find the electroplating process in use in this area today. It is a privilege to see companies such as J. Hudson and E.C. Williams using the latest forms of a process first developed in St Paul's Square and Newhall Street over one hundred and eighty years ago.

▶ Products typical of Georgian Birmingham, including buttons, buckles, japanned ware and one of the books printed by John Baskerville, photographed on a sculpture inspired by his work.

PUBLII VIRGILII
MARONIS
BUCOLICA,
GEORGICA,
ET
AENEIS.

BIRMINGHAMIÆ;
Typis JOHANNIS BASKERVILLE.
M DCC LXVI.

1: Background

The origins of Birmingham industry

Birmingham is first recorded as a small hamlet close to the River Rea, just south of where the Bull Ring and St Martin's Church are situated today. From its description in the Domesday survey of 1086 it seems to have been fairly insignificant, having just five villagers, four smallholders and a rental value of 20 shillings. The first signs of change came in 1166, when the De Birmingham family were successful in gaining a charter to hold a market.

The reasons behind the town's subsequent growth are complex. Geographical and geological factors were certainly involved. Sited where a mile-wide sandstone ridge (which runs south from Lichfield as far as Bromsgrove) meets less pervious ground, Birmingham benefitted from multiple sources of clean spring water. These, together with water from artesian wells, remained important in Birmingham from Anglo-Saxon times, through the Victorian era and even today. Deposits of sand of a type especially suited for moulding processes were also to prove important.

The frequent cycles of redevelopment that today's city centre has undergone have given plenty of scope for archaeological digs which have provided new information about Birmingham's past. Especially significant were investigations by the University of Birmingham Archaeological Department in the late 1990s, when the 1960s Bull Ring shopping centre was demolished. The excavation of the medieval moat which divided the town from the surrounding deer park, beneath what is now Selfridges and Park Street car park, was particularly important.

As the team of archaeologists dug down, the layering of debris in the moat revealed much of the timeline of industrial development from the middle ages on. There was

▶ Birmingham 'toys' – buttons and buckles typical of the style of metalwork produced in Birmingham in the 1700s and 1800s.

◀ Excavations in Edgbaston Street, Birmingham, 1999

evidence for the production of leather, ceramics and metal items which demonstrated that the medieval market town was also a manufacturing centre from as far back as the 1100s – much earlier than had been previously known. Analysis of crucible fragments gave evidence for the production of alloys of copper with zinc, lead and tin. Another dig in nearby Edgbaston Street found leather tanning pits from the 1200s.

All this demonstrates that Birmingham had moved on from being just a marketplace to actually producing the goods that they were selling.

Birmingham 'toys'

The 1600s were a period of increasing prosperity for Birmingham, which was developing into a significant manufacturing town. It was especially noted for its iron and steel 'toys', the name which was given to the numerous small metal products it made. However, the town had also, unfortunately, made a name for itself as a manufacturer of counterfeited coins and poor quality products. These items, produced across a variety of trades, were known disparagingly as 'brummagem ware'.

In the 1700s, the growing middle classes of Britain and Europe, keen to show off their new-found wealth through their household possessions, clothing and accessories, offered a rapidly increasing market for Birmingham's toy makers. William Hutton, in his History of Birmingham, reviewed the toy trades at the close of the 1700s. He described button making as pre-eminent, with changing fashions leading to 'astonishing consumption'. Button prices ranged widely from as little as 3d (less than 2p) up to 140 guineas (£147) per 'gross' of 144 items. After buttons, Hutton pointed to buckles, and especially the 'large square buckle plated with silver', as the must-have consumer products of the day. However, it was not an easy business to be in – Hutton also noted that, while there might be huge fortunes to be made, a 'far greater number submit to bankruptcy'.

Raw materials for the trade were often refined locally; steel was produced in the aptly named Steelhouse Lane, while a brass works was built alongside the new Birmingham Canal on what is now Broad Street, where its frontage can be seen to this day.

Birmingham was also a significant producer of guns, not only for private use and for the armed forces, but also for use in the slave trade. Guns were often bartered in exchange for those taken into enslavement on the West African coast. However, as with the inferior 'brummagem ware', the guns sold to slave traders also had a reputation as inferior products, which were brazenly dumped on the West African market.

A town with the freedom to act

The career of the industrialist John Baskerville (1706-1775) epitomises the factors behind Georgian Birmingham's success as an industrial centre. Baskerville came to Birmingham from Wolverley in Worcestershire a little before 1728. He set up as a letter engraver and

▶ Japanned papier-mâché snuff box with portrait of John Baskerville hand painted by Samuel Raven (after James Millar)

◄ Stone plaque with a sample of John Baskerville's early work as a letter cutter.

► Japanned crumb tray and boxes similar to those produced in Birmingham.

▼ Title page of Baskerville's smaller 1766 Latin edition of Virgil

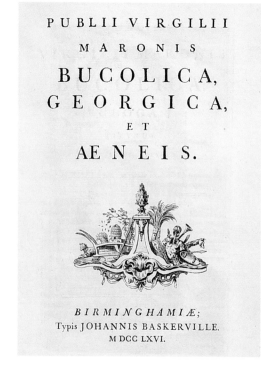

writing master in the centre of the town, close to today's Moor Street railway station. From there he was able to observe how the town's manufacturing businesses were booming. In particular, his interest was caught by the 'japanning' process. This imitation of far eastern decorative techniques was first brought to the town by John Taylor (1711-1775), who specialised in snuff boxes. In the japanning process, a decorative finish was built up using multiple layers of paint and varnish, heat treated between each layer to give a high-gloss, high-quality finish.

Baskerville went into the japanning trade himself. His business prospered and moved to bigger premises several times as it grew. As well as small items such as snuff boxes, he is thought to have produced larger wares such as tea trays, and he combined japanning with the process of moulding *papier-mâché* with great success (although it is unlikely, as is sometimes claimed, that he invented that process). In 1742, Baskerville applied for the first-ever japanning patent, which related to the production of japanned metal mouldings which could be used as veneers on picture frames and larger pieces of furniture. Unfortunately for us, japanned items were not normally given a maker's mark, so it is not possible to distinguish Baskerville's products from those of other manufacturers, such as Birmingham's most prolific maker Henry Clay or rival wares from Pontypool in South Wales.

The wealth which Baskerville accumulated allowed him to build Easy Hill, a grand

house alongside his manufactory, to which he moved in 1748. It also allowed him to revisit his earlier interest in lettering and he spent four years setting up a new printing business. The technical skills around him were key to his new endeavour. For example, the type punches needed for his revolutionary new Baskerville typeface were formed from hardened steel, while improvements to the engineering of his printing presses, to the paper and to the inks he used would all have been assisted by the skills available in the town. All this work culminated in 1757, when he printed and published his first book: the works of the Roman poet Virgil in quarto. He went on to print over sixty books, both at his Birmingham works and at the University of Cambridge.

Baskerville found that Birmingham gave him the freedom to act he needed. It was helpful that the town was not formally incorporated and was not restrained by the protectionism of the guild system, which controlled crafts and trades in places such as London and Bristol. His success demonstrated that Birmingham, on the verge of the Industrial Revolution, was somewhere you could come with an idea and move it forward without too much hindrance, and with a supportive network of skilled artisans on hand.

Baskerville's house was burnt down in the Priestley riots of 1791. The site now lies beneath Centenary Square, but he is remembered there with an artwork based on his revolutionary typeface design.

▶ Industry and Genius (David Patten, 1990). A Portland stone and bronze monument to the work of John Baskerville on the site of his house. It was inspired by the 'punches' used to create the Baskerville typeface in which his first book – Virgil – was printed.

The world's first manufactory

The production techniques and operating style of Birmingham's early Georgian manufacturers led the way for later industrialists. Foremost among these was Matthew Boulton (1728-1809) who was influenced, and some say also taught, by Baskerville. In 1759, when Boulton took over the family's small toy-making business in Snow Hill from his father, Matthew Boulton senior, he saw that it was the right time to move the business up a gear, both in scale of production and – to overcome the stigma of 'brummagem ware' – in quality. His father's small workshop employed perhaps a dozen people but, under Matthew Boulton junior, the business was transformed into the huge Soho Manufactory. Here, on Soho Heath, then on the town's northern outskirts, Boulton worked with up to twelve different business partners. They produced a diverse range of products including buckles, 'Sheffield' plate and 'ormolu' (gilded bronze), as well as japanned ware and even painted windows. Later in life, he set up the very large and successful Soho Mint on the site. To power production, Boulton turned to the new, efficient steam engine invented by James Watt (1736-1819) – and so was born a famous partnership which was to supply steam power to the world.

In Boulton's career we can identify approaches to business which continued to be fundamental into the Victorian era and indeed remain so today. He placed great importance on protecting his inventions with patents, and took firm action if they were infringed

▼ Portrait of Matthew Boulton by Sir William Beechey

– essential to the success of the steam engine business was the protection of a patent granted in 1775. He was also very politically astute – this is demonstrated by his efforts to get a local assay office established in Birmingham, for which he used intermediaries at Westminster, the equivalent of today's political lobbyists. Boulton befriended royalty and aristocracy across Europe, entertaining them at his home, Soho House, which overlooked the Manufactory. He arranged for visitors to take what must have been some of the earliest factory tours – though he had to beware of industrial spies. It was also at Soho House that the famous Lunar Society of industrialists and intellectuals sometimes met and dined together on nights when there was a full moon to guide their journey home.

Although the partnership of Boulton and Watt is particularly celebrated today, they represent just one among the many large-scale toy making enterprises which emerged in Birmingham as the Industrial Revolution took hold. The Soho Manufactory was later lost under a Victorian housing development, but Soho House still stands and is open to visitors – a fine example of the many grand houses which successful manufacturers built with their profits. We should not forget however, that those profits were often built on poor and hazardous working conditions and, not infrequently, were tainted by involvement in the slave trade.

▶ Ormolu Ewers (Boulton and Fothergill, c1762-1775). Produced at the Soho Manufactory, these use the rare mineral 'Blue John' which was mined only in the Peak District of Derbyshire. Boulton failed to secure a lease of the mines in 1768, but did manage to buy 14 tonnes of the precious material.

▼ Matthew Boulton's Soho Manufactory in an aquatint by Francis Eginton, after a drawing by John Phillip

The Colmore family and the Jewellery Quarter

Birmingham's famous Jewellery Quarter was built on land that had once belonged to St Thomas's Priory and extended from the present Priory Square, alongside Corporation Street, to Newhall Hill. After Henry VIII's split from the Church of Rome in 1537, England's monasteries were dissolved and their estates sold off. Part of the lands of St Thomas's was purchased by the Colmore family, who had come to the town from France in the 1400s as traders in wool and linen. They built themselves a country house named New Hall which was situated where today's Great Charles Street joins the inner ring road; Newhall Street now runs along the line of the elm avenue which once led to the house.

By the 1740s, the Colmore family had moved to Hendon on the outskirts of London and Ann Colmore obtained a private Act of Parliament to enable their Birmingham estate to be sold off in lots, on long leases. Within five years, development of the area alongside what is now Colmore Row was well under way and, as it continued under Ann's son Sir Charles

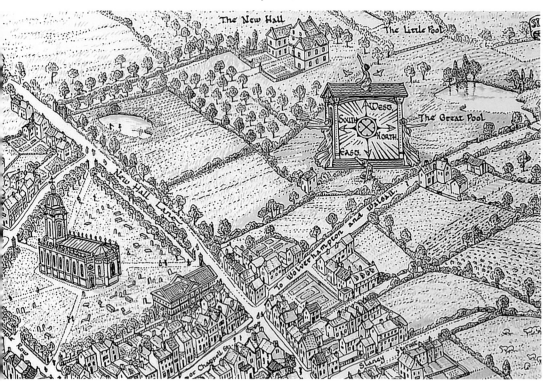

A PICTURE·MAP of BIRMINGHAM IN·1730·IMAGINED & DRAWN·FROM·CITY RECORDS by Bernard Sleigh ·19· and lettered by I. A Ellis ·23·

▲ ▶ A reconstruction of Birmingham as it might have looked in 1730 (Bernard Sleigh, 1923). The viewpoint is from the east, so north is to the right. The detail above shows St Philip's Church (now Cathedral), which was then on the edge of the town. The fields and parkland of the Colmore family's estate and their New Hall mansion can be seen beyond New Hall Lane, which would be renamed Ann Street after Ann Colmore, then later Colmore Row. The site on which St Paul's Church would be built is a little off the map to the right.

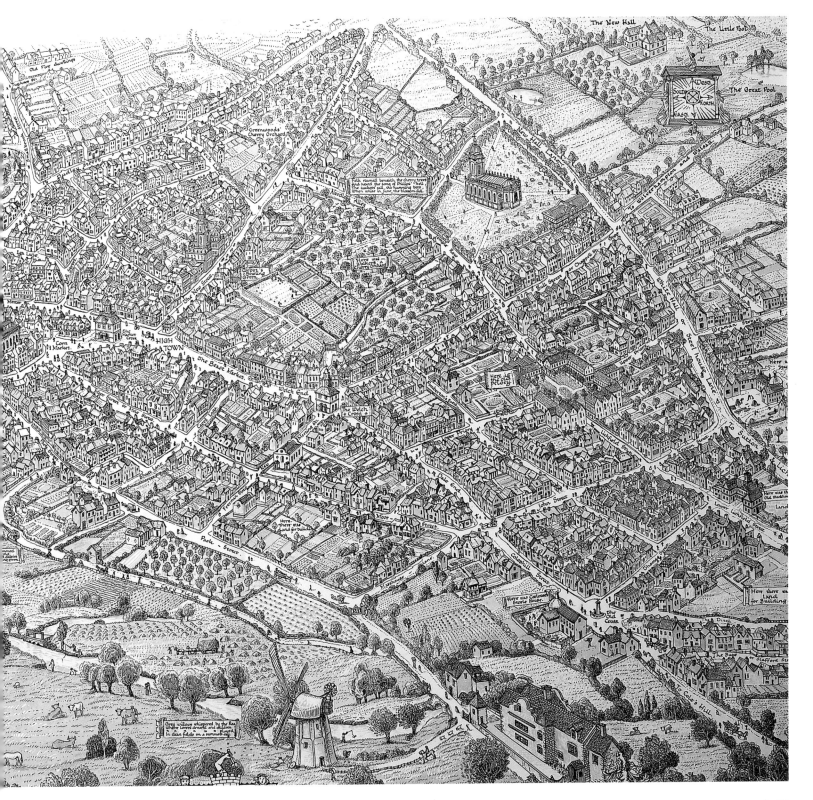

Colmore, new streets were named after his children Charles, Mary Anne, Lionel and Caroline. In 1795, the estate passed to Lionel, and in 1807 to his sister Caroline Colmore (1766-1837).

The development of the Colmore estate was closely linked with that of Birmingham's canals, especially important for bringing raw materials such as coal, limestone and part-finished metals from the Black Country to the new manufactories. In 1768, the Birmingham Canal Navigations company, whose promoters naturally included Matthew Boulton, commissioned the engineer James Brindley (1716-1772) to design a new canal. Its winding, contour-hugging route conveniently passed by the businesses of many of its shareholders.

New canals

Sir Charles Colmore astutely managed to obtain an agreement that the canal would have a terminus on his estate and so increase his land's development potential. However, this move encountered opposition from Boulton on the grounds of increased construction costs and the potential loss of crucial water supply to his works. Boulton dispatched fellow Lunar Society member William Small to London to oppose the canal's extension onto the Newhall Estate. But Sir Charles was well connected politically and for once Boulton received a bloody nose.

Eventually a compromise was reached which involved two canal terminuses, one arm going under what is now Broad Street to the coal wharves at Paradise Street (beneath today's HSBC headquarters) and another to finish on Colmore land at Newhall Wharf, beside the, by then empty, New Hall mansion.

In 1809, Caroline Colmore added a short canal arm from the Birmingham & Fazeley Canal to sand pits under Newhall Hill. These were important not just for building sand, but also for use in the moulding of metal castings, for which this sand was particularly suited. The canal was first known as Miss Colmore's Canal and later as Whitmore's Canal.

St Paul's Square

New Hall mansion was demolished in 1787 and little trace remains today of either the Newhall Branch or Miss Colmore's Canal, but they served their purpose in promoting the development of the Colmore estate for a mixture of business and housing. Detached villas for affluent professionals and business people were later joined by more modest terraced houses, often with workshops behind so they could serve as both a family home and a metalworking business.

In the 1770s, Sir Charles Colmore donated three acres of land and £1,000 to the Church of England for the building of a new church, St Paul's, to be designed by Wolverhampton architect Robert Eykin with the help of local man Samuel Wyatt. Both James Watt and

▶ St Paul's Church (Robert Eykin, Samuel Wyatt, 1779)

▼ Painted windows inside St Paul's Church (Francis Eginton, 1791). Eginton initially worked at the Soho Manufactory where he developed techniques for painting windows. Here the window depicts the conversion of St Paul from a study by the American artist Benjamin West .

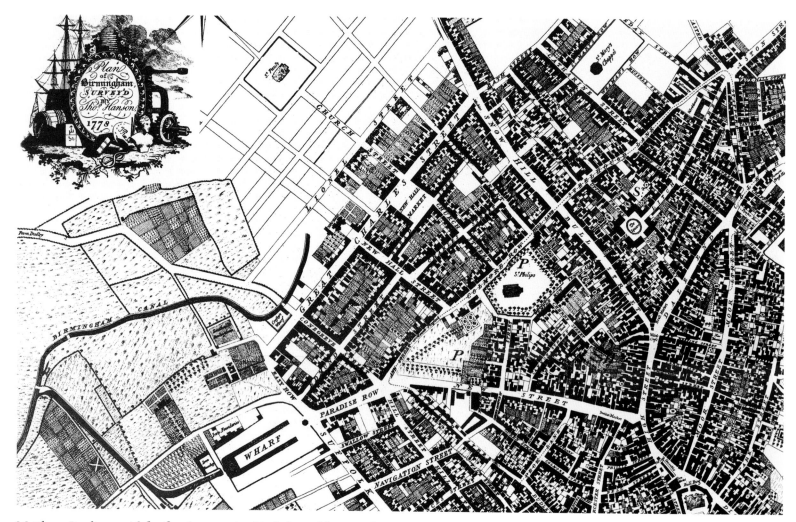

Matthew Boulton paid for family pews in this fashionable new church (although they remained loyal to St Mary's in Handsworth, where both are buried). St Paul's was consecrated in 1779, the upper part of the tower and spire being an addition of 1822-23. The unusual painted east window depicting the conversion of St Paul is by Francis Eginton, a former partner of Boulton, and is modelled on an altarpiece by Benjamin West.

Sir Charles' act of philanthropy was also a shrewd business move as St Paul's was to form the centrepiece of a new square. Around this, leases for fine Georgian town houses were to be sold to successful middle class families seeking to get away from the noise and grime of Birmingham town centre to an elegant Georgian square similar to the fashionable developments of the time in London, Bristol or Bath.

However, the development did not work out quite as intended. Such was the pressure for additional commercial premises in the town that, without modern 'change of use' restrictions, many of the plots of St Paul's Square ended up with workshops in the yards

▲ Birmingham in 1778, surveyed by Thomas Hanson (detail). The south eastern part of the Newhall estate, between Colmore Row and Great Charles Street, has already been developed. To the north west, roads have been laid out but building has only just begun. St Paul's Church stands isolated. New Hall mansion, next to the terminus of the Newhall Branch of the canal, has not yet been demolished.

▶ Cambrian Wharf, where the Newhall Branch of the canal now ends

behind and sometimes also trade or retail areas fronting onto the street. Although it did not offer the quiet seclusion envisioned, this mix of town centre living with noisy industry became a centre of inventiveness. The innovations produced in St Paul's Square and the Jewellery Quarter around it were to bring immense wealth to the city, and it is to some of those that we now turn our attention.

▶ Nineteenth century spectacles similar to those which James Elkington might have made, photographed in front of St Paul's Church.

2: Early Elkington

Industrious families

It was at number 60 St Paul's Square that James Elkington (1770-1843) had both his home and his business when he married Lydia Richards (1772-1830) in April 1799. James was an optician and manufacturer of spectacle frames in metal and other materials. He came from a farming family from Princethorpe in Warwickshire, where his father Joseph had achieved a little fame as a pioneer of land drainage techniques. Lydia came from an established Birmingham toy-making family – her brothers Josiah and George Richards ran a manufactory of gilt and silver products just a few steps away at 43-44 St Paul's Square.

James and Lydia's son George Richards Elkington (1801-1865) was born in St Paul's Square on 17 October 1801. In 1815, at the age of fourteen years, George was apprenticed to his uncles, later being made a partner in their firm, which in 1829 was re-styled as Richards and Elkington. George Elkington ran the Birmingham production operation, while uncle George Richards set up a shop in London's Holborn, retailing products including the then in vogue black and gilt jewellery worn during mourning. This was an early marker of the keen sense of fashion which guided George Elkington as a businessman. It was this emphasis on fashionable design which was to be key to the enduring success of the huge range of products later produced by Elkington & Co.

Another member of the Elkington family in St Paul's Square was Henry Elkington (1810-1852), son of James' brother John. Henry had arrived from Princethorpe in the 1820s to serve as an apprentice in his uncle James' spectacle making business.

▲ Portrait of George Richards Elkington (Samuel West, 1865)

◀ Georgian town houses in St Paul's Square

▶ Front door of 12 St Paul's Square. The houses in which the Elkington and Richards families lived and work do not survive, but they would have been in a similar style.

New spectacles

George Elkington inherited his father's optical business around 1824. The foundation in metalworking techniques he had gained while apprenticed to his uncles was to benefit this company too, resulting in several new developments in spectacle design. George's Patent No. 6692 of 1834 covered two related innovations. The first was for double spectacles where the lower lens was angled inwards so that when looking down to read the wearer could look through the glass straight on rather than obliquely. The second, which he named 'pantoscopic spectacles', was intended for long-sighted wearers: the single lenses were again angled for reading, but the frames were specially shaped with high joints, high bridge and a flattened top rim so that long-sighted wearers could easily look over the top for distance viewing. Although these products never took off in a big way, the second design is the ancestor of the 'PRO' (pantoscopic round oval) and 'half eye' styles of frame which are widely used today. It is also interesting to note George's early use of the patent process to protect his designs.

By the mid 1830s, George Elkington and his cousin Henry had both received a thorough grounding in metalworking and the production of small consumer items in the family firms. One of the most important techniques they and the other toymakers around them relied on was the gilding and silver plating of metal – it was to the improvement of these processes that they next turned their minds.

▶ Spectacles from the collection of the College of Optometrists, similar to those shown in George Elkington's patent of 1834. The double spectacles (bottom left) were probably made by Elkington, the other 'pantoscopic' design might also have been.

◀ Extract from the diagram which accompanied George Elkington's 1834 spectacle frame Patent No. 6692.

Traditional gilding and silver plating

Layering precious metal onto the surface of a cheaper metal base, to make it appear as if an item had been formed of solid gold or silver, was an essential and increasingly important technique for Birmingham's toymakers. Plated products could be produced for a fraction of the price of an item made out of solid precious metal – and yet be almost undistinguishable from the real thing.

The growth in gilding and plating in the 1700s brought an increasing realisation that traditional techniques were not only technically demanding but also in some cases very hazardous to health. Although there were a number of large manufactories such as Boulton's, toymaking was still predominantly a craft business, carried out in small workshops often close to people's homes, so these health issues had an impact not only on those employed in the metalworking industries, but also on their families and neighbours.

Traditional gilding was the process most hazardous to health. Ground gold was added to mercury which had been heated to just under its boiling point. Excess mercury was removed by filtering through chamois leather and the resulting amalgam was layered onto the item being gilded. This was then fired to burn off the mercury, leaving a layer of gold. The finished product often went by the name of 'ormolu'. This process was widely used in Birmingham, including at the Soho Manufactory, as well as in other cities such as London and Paris. Silver provided the best base for gilding but copper alloys such as 'German silver' (which despite its name is actually a mixture of copper with zinc and nickel) were much cheaper.

In experienced hands, mercury gilding could result in excellent gold layering with stunning results, but its health issues were already becoming apparent by the time the Elkington and Richards families were working in the toy trade. In Paris, which had seen a particular boom in gilding after the French Revolution, the problem was already well understood by 1820.

Back in Birmingham, in 1821 local physician Dr John Darwell presented a paper on the health hazards of mercury vapour and the shaking palsy it produced. Darwell noted that, in small-scale gilding operations, the burning-off process was often done using an open frying pan on a stove. He described the impact on the gilder, which started with shaking, convulsions and salivation, then moved on to mental illness and paralysis (it is perhaps no coincidence that the town's new asylum was built close to the toy making industry's centre in the Jewellery Quarter). Darwell described some safety features which had already improved matters in the button making industry, where mercury was burnt off within an enclosed iron vessel. He also found a worker who had been gilding for 38 years without symptoms who claimed that it was his "frequent ablutions and never eating without this precaution" that had protected him.

For silver plating, the issues driving change in production techniques were somewhat different. While not so hazardous to health, the traditional process was difficult and had

▶ Toymaker's houses in Ann Street, photographed shortly before their demolition c.1873 for a redevelopment which included the building of the Council House. Ann Street, formerly New Hall Lane and now Colmore Row, was named after Ann Colmore. The houses show elements typical of toymaker's premises, with high chimneys to remove toxic fumes from the hearth.

The bronze statue of Sir Robert Peel produced by Elkington can be seen in the foreground in its original location (see page 51).

▼ Street sign for Colmore Row, as Ann Street is named today

serious limitations. This process was known as 'Sheffield' plating after the city in which it was invented and most famously used, although the same process was also used in Birmingham and elsewhere. Thin sheets of silver were heat laminated onto base sheets of copper or copper alloy, which could then be shaped into cutlery or other items. The resulting product had a fairly thick layer of silver and so was relatively resistant to wear, but the process was not suitable for the plating of complex shapes, so the naturalistic designs full of curves and dimples which were so beloved of the early Victorians could not be reproduced well. Edges were also a particular problem and had to be separately covered with edge beading (a feature which was sometimes retained in later designs, even though no longer technically necessary). Poorly executed silver plating was likely to be classed as 'brummagem ware', a stigma with which no toymaking family wanted to be labelled.

Immersion gilding

Working in St Paul's Square in their several businesses, George Richards Elkington and his younger cousin Henry had the foresight to see that the gilding and silvering techniques in use all around them were neither satisfactory nor sustainable. They also had the ability to draw on the reservoir of industrial experience which surrounded them, as well as on the latest scientific discoveries from across Europe, and apply those to the needs of their fast-growing businesses – and so embark on a journey of radical change. This was a journey in stages, and progress of their process of invention was marked by the lodging of successive patents.

Initially, the Elkingtons became interested in plating using precious metals dissolved in hot solutions. George took out a patent for an 'immersion gilding' process in 1836. His patent describes how strings of toys, made of copper alloy, could be dipped for a few seconds into a boiling alkaline solution of gold to emerge covered in a thin layer of that precious metal. The patent claimed that this new process could produce both a better appearance and better durability than mercury gilding and, also very importantly, had a much lower health risk associated with it. In 1837, cousin Henry got in on the act with patents for improved immersion gilding and for silver plating by immersion, although in practice when using this method silver did not adhere to the base metal as well as gold.

The excellent results obtained from immersion gilding, together with competitive pricing, meant that it was soon widely adopted and the use of hazardous mercury-based gilding began to decline. The process was particularly popular in France, where it became known there as *la liqueur Elkington*. However, some Parisian platers attempted to ignore the need to licence the use of the process from its Birmingham inventors, which meant that the Elkingtons had to defend their patents in the French courts – experience which they would find very useful in protecting their later patents.

The profits from the use and licensing of the immersion gilding process were so

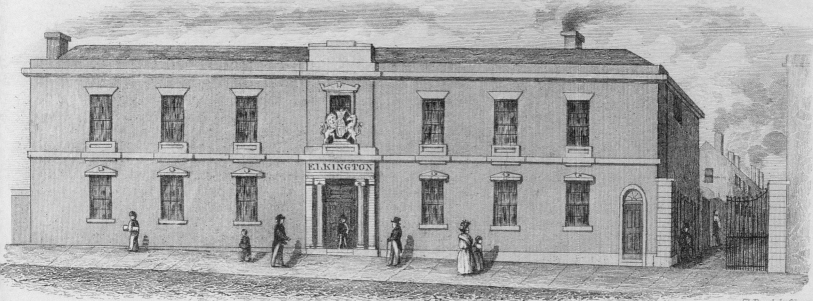

Advertisement for G. R. Elkington & Co. from *Osborne's London & Birmingham Railway Guide* (1840). Note that the emphasis is on providing gilding services to the trade, using the newly patented immersion gilding process, rather than on manufacturing items.

significant that, in 1838, George Elkington was able to expand the business, investing in a new factory in Newhall Street, just around the corner from St Paul's Square. He formed a new company, G. R. Elkington & Co., in partnership with several prominent toymaker associates. These included, for example, John Hardman junior (1812-67) who was heir to a family button making business and would soon found an important stained glass studio in the Jewellery Quarter. George Elkington's new company offered immersion gilding services to its associates and other businesses around the Jewellery Quarter. However, its life would be limited as the immersion process would soon be superseded by George and Henry's next invention.

▶ Two-pronged pie/pastry forks (1925), photographed by the pool at Woodbrooke, the family home of George Elkington in Selly Oak.

3: Electroplating

The new science of electricity

By the late 1830s, all the pieces were falling into place for the Elkington cousins. On the one hand, there was a huge expansion in demand for new products which needed to be met, on the other was hundreds of years of expertise, now galvanised by the drive of the Industrial Revolution and by new advances in science. Pioneers of the 1700s such as Baskerville, Boulton and Watt had already shown how powerful the bringing together of science and industry could be. Now, moving into the 1800s, there were new scientific discoveries just waiting for the right people to apply them to industrial processes. Among those discoveries was electricity, and among those right people were the Elkingtons – the combination resulted in innovations which would not only make their fortunes, but also revolutionise manufacturing around the world.

To understand how this all came about let's go back to Italy in 1799, to the laboratory of physicist Alessandro Volta (1745-1827) at the University of Padua. Here Volta constructed columns of silver and zinc plates, linked with electrolytic pads, which resulted in the production of electricity – in fact the first battery. The following year, Volta described his discovery in a letter to the President of the Royal Academy in London and experiments in England using 'Volta's pile' quickly followed. The English chemist William Wollaston (1766-1828) was among those to observe the deposition of thin layers of metal when using a voltaic pile. Similar experiments were carried out in 1801 in France and Germany, and soon the electrochemical deposition of silver, copper and tin had all been demonstrated. In 1805, Italian chemist Luigi Valentino Brugnatelli (1761-1818), Volta's friend and contemporary at Padua, used the phenomenon to achieve the electrodeposition of a layer of gold onto two large silver medals. In 1812, English scientist Michael Faraday (1791-1867) also experimented with voltaic piles and noted that when he separated the copper and zinc discs some were coated with the other metal. He concluded that the metals had passed through the solution between them and pronounced that it was 'well worth notice' as 'no effect takes place without a cause'.

However, perhaps because of the Napoleonic Wars, this early work was largely ignored and it was not until 1832 that Faraday would conduct further electrochemistry experiments which would give rise to his two laws of electrolysis. Another advance came when John Frederic Daniell (1790-1845), professor of Chemistry at King's College, London invented the Daniell cell, an improved source of DC electricity which could provide a current much more constant and reliable than Volta's original battery. The race to commercialise this new science was on.

Electroplating envisioned

By the late 1830s the Elkingtons were busy on all fronts. They were still running several family businesses, filing patents for immersion gilding, and moving to new industrial

▲ Portrait of Alessandro Volta

▶ Chamberstick (1875, pattern 9010) and wick trimmer (1845). The ideal length of a candle wick is between one eighth to a quarter of an inch. Wick trimmers helped to maintain this length, collecting the snipped wick in a trimmings box. These early trimmers also have a metal partition in the trimmings box so that old trimmings end up in the back to be emptied at a later date. This early piece shows signs that it may have been made with a mixture of electroplating and traditional silvering techniques for the handles.

premises. They were also working to implement and improve their immersion plating techniques, to which end they employed several men from the local brass industry, including Alexander Parkes, a brass caster, who we will meet again later. But, not content with all this they also undertook a major research project to develop a commercially viable electroplating process.

An early sign of this new interest was a patent filed in 1838 describing the coating of copper and brass with zinc using electrical current rather than hot solutions. But it was on 25th March 1840 that George and Henry Elkington took a huge leap of faith, filing Patent No. 8447 which described the use of silver solutions and 'galvanic current' to plate items.

Once filed, the cousins had just six months to finalise the patent by supplying full details of the methods that would be protected by it. The work to fine-tune their techniques so that the patent properly described and protected their new processes was substantial. It included adjusting the salt concentration in the plating bath and the power of the batteries to make the technique suitable for mass production. The patent as originally filed described the use of ammonia solutions together with gold and silver salts. However, that was soon to change, with the perhaps surprising, but very timely, help of a local surgeon.

The adventurous Dr Wright

John Wright (1808-1844) had trained as a surgeon in Edinburgh, Paris, and London and had come to work in the Bordesley Green area on the east side of Birmingham. He had an enthusiastic personality and craved excitement both at home and work. Around this time, some in the medical profession were keen to consider whether electricity had any potential uses in medicine and so in his spare time Wright began to experiment with Daniell's new battery. In 1839, having read about the behaviour of solutions of potassium cyanide, he began to experiment with using these as electrolytes for electroplating. When he tried cyanide salts, he found that he could get an even and long-lasting coating of gold and silver onto a copper base.

The Elkingtons were now rushing to finalise their patent details. How they and John Wright came together – whether through local contacts or via a London patent agent – is not entirely clear. The Elkingtons asked a chemist in London to check out Wright's claims, and it was confirmed that cyanide salts did indeed enhance the plating process, and so they agreed to add Wright's specification of potassium cyanide to their final patent. They only had time to draw up an informal agreement with Wright, paying him £300 initially and £500 on submission of the patent. Wright would also receive a generous royalty of a shilling per ounce of silver that the Elkingtons plated, and a third of any income from third parties licensing the patent.

Wright's work was central to the new plating techniques and he was clearly excited to see his home experiments scaled up to industrial production. Indeed, he gave up his

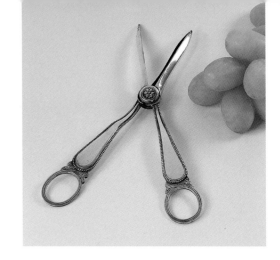

▲ ▶ Grape shears (1849). Designed to ensure that grapes, popular as part of the dessert course, were eaten in the correct 'polite' manner. The handles are longer than the blades and the end is blunt so as not to damage the fruit. The lower blade includes a flange so the grapes can be transferred to the plate without touching them.

▼ First page of George and Henry Elkington's electroplating patent No. 8847 of 1840

A.D. 1840 . . . . N° 8447.

Plating Metals.

G. R. AND H. ELKINGTON'S SPECIFICATION.

TO ALL TO WHOM THESE PRESENTS SHALL COME, we, GEORGE RICHARDS ELKINGTON and HENRY ELKINGTON, of Birmingham, in the County of Warwick, Gentlemen, send greeting.

WHEREAS Her present most Excellent Majesty Queen Victoria, by Her Letters Patent under the Great Seal of Great Britain, bearing date at Westminster, the Twenty-fifth day of March, in the third year of Her reign, did, for Herself, Her heirs and successors, give and grant unto us, the said George Richards Elkington and Henry Elkington, Her especial licence, full power, sole privilege and authority, that we, the said George Richards Elkington and Henry Elkington, our exors, admors, and assigns, or such others as we, the said George Richards Elkington and Henry Elkington, our exors, admors, or assigns, should at any time agree with, and no others, from time to time and at all times during the term of years therein expressed, should and lawfully might make, use, exercise, and vend, within England, Wales, and the Town of Berwick-upon-Tweed, our Invention of "IMPROVEMENTS IN COATING, COVERING, OR PLATING CERTAIN METALS;" in which said Letters Patent is contained a proviso that we, the said George Richards Elkington and Henry Elkington, or one of us, shall cause a particular description of the nature of our said Invention, and in what manner the same is to be performed, to be inrolled in Her said Majesty's

◄ The Elkington electroplating room in an engraving from Sheridan Muspratt's 1857 book on chemistry. Note the viewing gallery from which visitors on a factory tour could watch the process.

▶ Cruet sets (left 1965; right pattern 37260). Salt, pepper and mustard condiment sets came in various designs for home and commercial use. They often feature 'Bristol blue' glass liners in the salt and mustard pots.

medical practice, moved to Great Charles Street, just up the road from the factory, and took charge of the electrochemical baths, making sure they became a commercially successful industrial process. Unfortunately, John Wright's adventurous nature extended to his hobby of racing his dog cart around Birmingham. This dangerous practice, illegal in London since 1839 but only banned nationwide in 1854, is reputed to have led to his untimely death at the age of just 35 when he fell from his cart.

New partnerships

The Elkingtons must have been certain that they had a success on their hands. Their patent was in place and they set up a new company, Elkington & Co., in which Henry now joined George as a partner. Their emphasis was shifting from providing plating services to other makers to manufacturing and plating their own products, including a range of high quality artistic and sculptural items for which Henry was largely responsible. Things were promising, but they were also astute enough to realise that they needed more capital and expertise if their business was to reach full potential. They knew where to turn.

Josiah Mason (1795-1881) was arguably Birmingham's most successful businessman. He had come to Birmingham from the carpet manufacturing town of Kidderminster. In his new town he worked in several metal industries, including a factory producing split rings, which helped him devise a new way to mass-produce pen nibs. Working with Mr Perry, a stationer from Manchester, he founded a new company and built a large factory at

▼ Portrait bust of Josiah Mason in Erdington (William Bloye after Francis John Williamson)

▶ Round toast rack (1910). Toast racks were a staple of the hospitality industry. This small wire ring version was produced in the early twentieth century, probably to an earlier design. It has a total of eleven metal pieces soldered together and seventeen solder points.

◀ Arched toast rack (1955). The main frame has been formed by shaping a pre-cut flat sheet that is then secured by a horizontal sheet. The handle is soldered to the central separator. In contrast to the earlier design shown on the right, this has just three metal pieces and only four solder points.

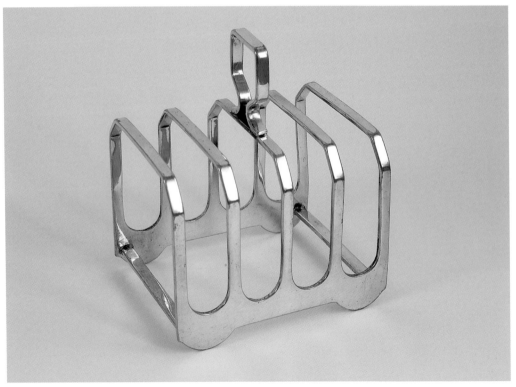

◀ Square toast rack, produced using similar techniques to the arched rack above.

41

▲ ▶ Teapots (above 1858, pattern 2002; right 1867, pattern 5887). Comprising eight to ten separate metal pieces and bone or ivory insulation on the handles. Though produced nine years apart they have the same basic design with different finishing and adornments. A matching cream jug (1874, pattern 2002) is also shown.

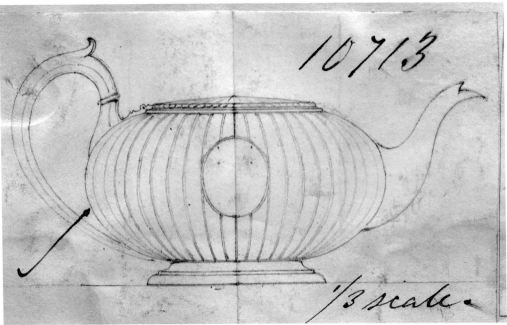

◀ Design from the Elkington pattern books. The body, spout and handle are all of a similar shape to the examples photographed, but the design features different decoration.

Lancaster Street, the site of which is close to today's Aston University. Mason's firm, along with others such as the Mitchell brothers and Joseph Gillott, made the Jewellery Quarter a global centre of pen nib production, at its height supplying 80% of the world's nibs – and Josiah Mason ran the biggest firm of them all.

On joining with the Elkingtons in 1842, Mason brought with him not just capital but also proven expertise in the design of large-scale factories for the production of small metal items in vast quantities. There were around 12 steps to pen nib production and many of them, especially rolling, shaping and finishing, would have had direct relevance to the processes in the Elkington works. So, it was a clever business decision by the Elkingtons to get Mason involved, and also to allow him to take the lead in areas where he had a successful track record and could help the company to grow.

Mason was to remain a partner until 1861, during which time the firm was known as Elkington, Mason & Co., after which the company's name reverted to Elkington & Co. The older partnership which George had formed with other local toy-makers, G. R. Elkington & Co., was wound up in 1843.

Mass production

It is Josiah Mason who should probably receive most credit for the expansion of the Newhall Street factory in the mid-1840s and again in the early 1850s. Ultimately, this factory would spread over a site of more than two acres and employ around a thousand workers. It straddled both the Birmingham & Fazeley Canal and Miss Colmore's Canal to

▼ The Elkington Newhall Street works in 1851 from *Cornish's Stranger's Guide Through Birmingham*

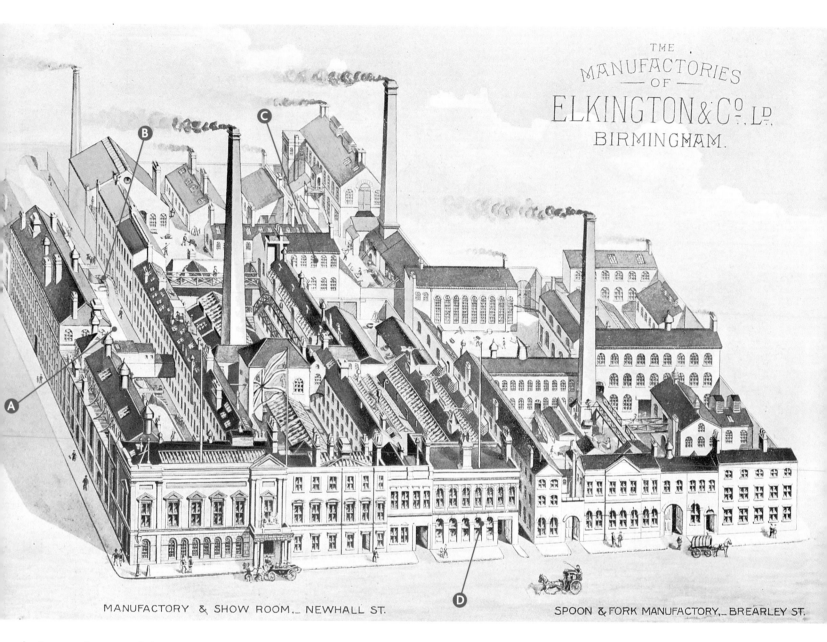

THE
MANUFACTORIES
OF
ELKINGTON & CO. LD.
BIRMINGHAM.

MANUFACTORY & SHOW ROOM._ NEWHALL ST.

SPOON & FORK MANUFACTORY,_ BREARLEY ST.

▲ The Manufactories of Elkington & Co. Ltd in 1906. The Newhall Street works is shown on the left next to the Brearley Street factory on the right – in reality the two were entirely separate.

The Birmingham & Fazeley Canal, which passes right through the Newhall Street site, is marked A. The entrance to the Whitmore Arm can just be seen at B. The surviving warehouse, which was on the site of Whitmore's foundry before it was incorporated into the Elkington site, is marked C. The surviving part of the Newhall Street frontage of Elkington factory is marked D.

the sandpit quarry under Newhall Hill. In the 1850s, a showroom was added, occupying the whole of the top floor on Newhall Street. It is interesting that the metalworking display rooms in the Victoria and Albert Museum, built some years later, appear remarkably similar to the now lost Elkington showrooms. Additional factories were built, including a large works in Brearley Street, close to Mason's pen nib factory. This was constructed between 1848 and 1851 for the mass production of silver-plated flatware, which Mason himself had probably identified as a key area for expansion.

As the factories grew, so did the need for a suitable electricity supply. The Woolrich Electrical Generator, which can now be seen in Thinktank, Birmingham Science Museum, was the earliest generator used in the electroplating industrial process. It was built at the

▲ Dessert spoons (1852-3). These simple spoons are typical of the everyday flatware items which were produced in the Brearley Street works after Josiah Mason joined the company.

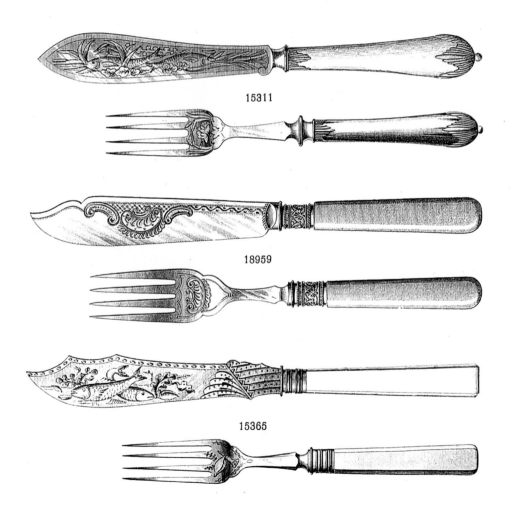

FISH EATING KNIVES AND FORKS,

15311

18959

15365

◀ Illustrations of a selection of fish knives and forks from an Elkington catalogue, giving some idea of the variety of designs the firm produced.

▶ A Woolrich Electrical Generator is displayed at Thinktank, Birmingham Science Museum. This example was supplied to Elkington for use in electroplating in 1844 and is believed to be the first ever electrical generator to provide electricity for an industrial process.

Magneto Works of Thomas Prime and Son, to a design by John Stephen Woolrich (1820–1850). In August 1842, Woolrich was granted a patent for his generator as a source of DC electricity to replace batteries. He offered to sell the rights to Elkington for the then enormous sum of £15,000. Not surprisingly the offer was declined. In the end, Elkington agreed to pay Woolrich £100 upfront and then £400 annually for the rest of the term of the patent. Woolrich later re-licensed the patent himself to use in his Magneto-Plating and Gilding Works in Great Charles Street, Birmingham. In 1849, he was listed as a 'chemist & magneto-plater and gilder', residing at 12 James Street, just off St Paul's Square in the Jewellery Quarter.

▲ Engraving of a Woolrich Electrical Generator at work in the Elkington electroplating room. This model has more magnets than the 1844 model at Thinktank. The figure in the foreground holds a 'string' of items for dipping in the plating baths behind.

▶ Electrotyped ewer, photographed in front of the Whitmore Warehouse on the Elkington site.

4: Art-Manufactures

Josiah Mason's emphasis on making useful items such as tableware and cutlery provided the mainstay of Elkington's business, but the company were also active in the finer arts, an area of work which resulted in some of their most famous and prestigious productions.

Art-Manufactures

The more artistic products made by Elkington, including ornamental plate and statuary, sometimes went under the name of 'Henry Elkington's Art-Manufactures'. The company worked with many sculptors and artists of the day (see chapter 5) and it is this work which took pride of place in the Elkington showroom, attracting public attention and so helping to enhance the early reputation of the firm – and to assist the sales of its more everyday products. One fine example of this sort of work in Birmingham is the cast bronze statue of Sir Robert Peel outside the police training college.

▶ Sir Robert Peel (Peter Hollins, 1855). This statue was produced by traditional casting at the Elkington Newhall Street works. Originally located in the town centre (see page 28), it has been sited outside the Police Training Centre since 1963.

▼ Coloured engraving of the Elkington showroom at the Newhall Street factory

Electrotyping

While the Peel statue was produced as a traditional casting, from early on the company had built on its expertise in electroplating to perfect the allied technique of 'electrotyping' (today more usually known as 'electroforming').

The electrotyping process used the ability of electricity to move metal ions out of solution to go beyond just forming a thin coating on an existing object and, by laying down metal into a mould, to create a whole new solid object. Henry Elkington took the lead in the company's electrotyping activities and Alexander Parkes was also closely involved, running this section of the factory in the 1840s.

The process was simple and elegant in principle. You would take an item that you wanted to copy and make an impression of it. The surface of the resulting mould would be made conductive, for example by painting a layer of lead onto it, so that when the mould was used as the cathode it was ready to receive metal deposited out of the electrolyte. When the current was turned on, a new item would start to appear almost as if by magic. If the anode were made out of metal then this would slowly dissolve and the electrolyte would be replenished as the new item was formed.

Owing to the mix of techniques which were used by Elkington, it is not always easy to ascertain if a sculptural piece by them was produced by traditional methods, by electrical processes, or a mixture of both. For example, most of the 18 statues which Elkington manufactured for the House of Lords had a core of cast zinc which had first been electroplated with copper and then finished by tinting and gilding.

A Royal visit

Just as Matthew Boulton had in the eighteenth-century, the Elkingtons understood that friends in high places were important to help oil the wheels of commerce and industry. Their factory and showrooms received visits from the Royal family, eminent Americans, the aristocracy of Europe, and the influential journalists of the day. Contemporary illustrations of the factory's main electroplating room show a viewing gallery, much as one might expect to find on a factory tour today (see page 38). The Newhall Street visitor's books, many of which have sadly been lost, were full of collectable signatures.

In November 1843, recently married Queen Victoria's twenty-four-year-old husband Prince Albert came to visit the Elkington factory. Prince Albert was looking to carve out a role for himself and was fast becoming a promoter of good art and design and its importance in taking industry forward. Modern science was exciting and the newly developed techniques being applied in Newhall Street – one of the first major industrial uses for electricity – was exactly the sort of cutting edge technology which the young Prince wanted to champion.

▲ ▶ 'Briot' Ewer (c 1880). Produced from moulds designed by Benjamin Schlick after a Renaissance pewter ewer by François Briot, which is in the V&A collection. The piece was first electrotyped in copper and then electroplated in both silver and gold. Much of the silver plate has worn away, revealing the underlying copper. The gilding has survived better.

The Great Exhibition of 1851

Prince Albert was determined that manufacturers should place greater emphasis on good design. To this end he encouraged the staging of the Great Exhibition of 1851, housed in the specially built 'Crystal Palace' in Hyde Park, as a showcase to the world. Similar exhibitions had already been held in France and were to prove a key marketing tool for Victorian commerce, both nationally and internationally. So keen was Albert to emphasise the importance of good design that he even suggested, although unsuccessfully, that more prominence should be given to the names of the designers than the manufacturers.

The glass and ironwork for the exhibition building were sourced from Birmingham and the Black Country, and many Birmingham companies exhibited. Elkington saw the Great Exhibition as an important opportunity to promote their products and had a major presence. They showed elaborate electroplated and electrotyped work, much of it to designs commissioned from contemporary artists.

▶ Large Tazza (1882). The body of this piece was formed by traditional methods. Featuring a family crest of an antelope on the centrepiece, it has been elaborately constructed from multiple decorated pieces with detailed finishing.

▼ The Crystal Palace from Dickinsons' *Comprehensive pictures of the Great Exhibition of 1851*

▼ ▶ Tazza Comport (1874/5, pattern 13509). In contrast to the Tazza on the previous page, this piece was made by electrotyping. The same electrotype mould was also used for a dish without a pedestal (pattern 13511). The wear to the silver plating, revealing the copper below, can be seen on the details of the cherubs.

The exhibition was a great success for Elkington. Their products proved very popular with the public and the subsequent expansion of their Birmingham premises was probably a direct result. The views of the artistic world were more mixed however and the start of a strong critical reaction against the elaborate naturalistic style can be discerned. Some even said that the exhibition merely demonstrated just how bad English design could be – certainly many of the items on display would not be to present-day tastes!

As a whole, the exhibition was phenomenally successful. The public came in great numbers and a substantial windfall profit was generated. After the event, encouraged by Prince Albert, much of this profit was invested in the purchase of land in South Kensington on which museums and educational institutions were to be established which would continue to promote the successful interaction of science and the arts – as indeed they do to this day. Elkington was to play an important part in this legacy too.

Electrotypes and the V&A

One of the projects made possible by the success of the Great Exhibition was the establishment of a Museum of Manufactures, through which Prince Albert's vision for the role of art and design in industry could be promoted. Originally based at Marlborough House, in 1857 it moved to new, purpose-built premises in Exhibition Road, eventually receiving its current name, 'The Victoria and Albert Museum', in 1899.

The Museum's Director, Henry Cole (1808-1882), was keen to make the institution's

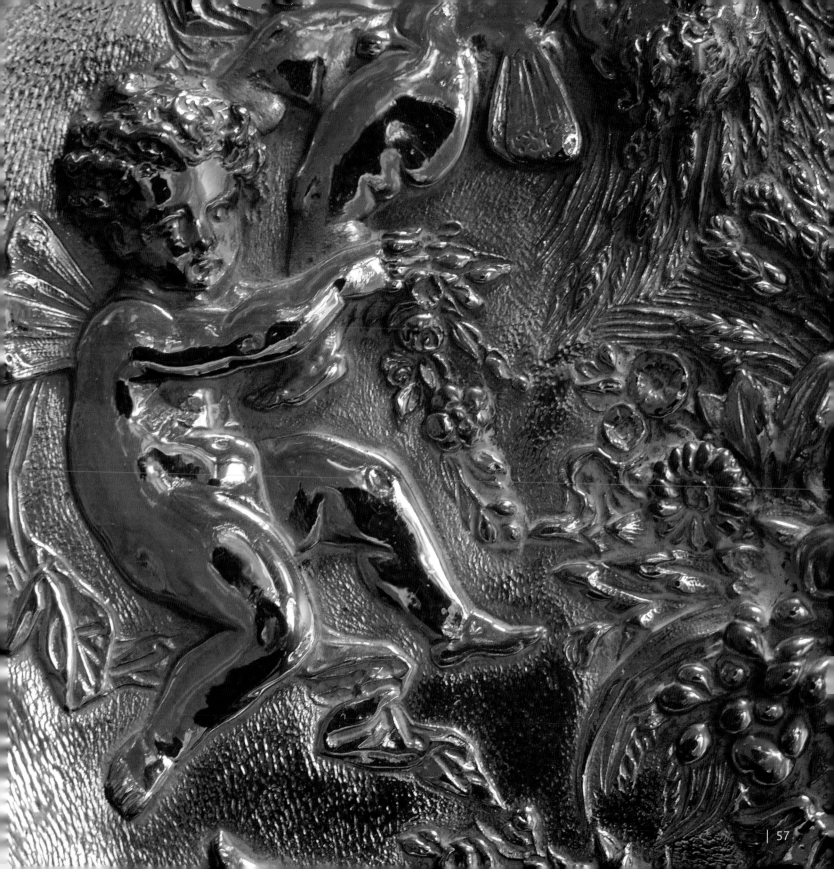

◀ Mosaic memorial to Henry Cole on the ceramic staircase at the V&A (1878), by his niece Florence Cole.

collection as comprehensive as possible. Cole was evangelistic in promoting interest in art and described the Museum as a 'schoolroom for everyone'. It was part of an art education process which became known as the 'South Kensington system'. But, given the difficulty and cost of obtaining the originals of great works of art, Cole determined to increase the collection by using copies. To this end he turned to the new art of photography and, for larger sculptural items, to the old art of plaster casting. For smaller works however, the remarkably accurate copies which could be made using Elkington's new electrotyping process were perfect.

So began a relationship which would last for sixty years. Elkington established a workshop in London where they could make moulds of original works of art which the Museum had borrowed from private collections. From these, primary electrotypes (or 'type patterns') were made in copper, from which secondary moulds could be made to manufacture multiple copies. Where the Museum's contract with an object's owner allowed, Elkington made multiple copies, some for show in the Museum and others to sell or lend to museums and art schools around the country who were not in a position to purchase original works of art. Further copies were sold to museums abroad, and to private collectors.

This relationship produced some remarkable copies – sometimes priceless works in their own right. Today the most famous of the Elkington products of this era is the Venus

▶ Ashleigh Barty, 2021 Wimbledon ladies singles champion, holding the Venus Rosewater Basin (1864). This partially gilded silver electrotype was first presented at Wimbledon in 1886.

Rosewater Basin. This silver and part-gilded electrotype was copied in 1864 from a plaster cast taken from a pewter original by Caspar Enderlein in the Louvre in Paris (itself a copy of a work by François Briot). Since 1886, it has been presented to the Wimbledon ladies singles champion. Another electrotype of this can be seen in Birmingham Museum and Art Gallery's Elkington collection.

Perhaps more famous than the Rosewater Basin in its own day was a piece known as the Milton Shield. This was designed and made by Leonard Morel-Ladeuil (1820-1888), who had learnt his trade in Paris where he had produced acclaimed work but found relations difficult with an industry which was conservative and resistant to change. In 1859, Elkington recruited Morel-Ladeuil, offering him a degree of artistic freedom he had struggled to find in Paris. He stayed with the company for twenty-three years. The shield is one of the most virtuoso pieces of metalwork to survive from the nineteenth century.

The Milton Shield depicts scenes from the poet John Milton's epic *Paradise Lost* and was commissioned for the 1867 Paris Exhibition. Work started in 1865 and the piece, which includes intricate pressing, chasing and hammering of silver and steel with gold wire inlay, took over a year to produce. In Paris both the artist and Elkington received a Gold Medal. Upon the shield's return, Elkington put on a touring exhibition of the work around its British show rooms. Electrotype copies of the Milton Shield were sold around the world, but the original was purchased for the nation in 1868, for the then enormous sum of £2,000, by what is now the Victoria and Albert Museum where it is displayed today.

Another large-scale electrotype on display at the V&A is the Jerningham Wine Cooler (see pages 62-63). This is a copy of an original in the Winter Palace in St Petersburg in Russia. Obtaining permission to make moulds from this, as well as from other items in the Russian Royal collection, was something of a coup and had involved diplomatic negotiations at the very highest level. This piece attracted particular attention in Britain when it was discovered that it had in fact been made in London and hallmarked in Goldsmith's Hall in 1734. Due to the size and complexity of the piece the process of making the moulds to send back home for electrotyping was particularly challenging and took around two weeks to complete.

Electroplating ceramics

Another, less well known Elkington collaboration was to produce silver-plated ceramic items in conjunction with the world-famous pottery firm Wedgwood.

As ceramics are not conductive they cannot be directly electroplated. However, Elkington were able to achieve electroplating using a technique similar to that employed to make the mould for an electrotype conductive. The area to be plated, which might be the whole of the outside of the piece or just a small portion such as the rim, was first coated with black lead before being electroplated with a copper base coat, after which a top coat of silver plate was applied.

▶ The original Milton Shield (Leonard Morel-Ladeuil, Elkington & Co., 1866).

▼ Wedgwood jug, silver-plated by Elkington (c1895). Note that the inside of the jug has not been plated. The copper base coat can be seen where the silver has worn through on the high points of the relief decoration.

▲ ▶ The 1884 V&A electrotype of the
Jerningham Wine Cooler on public display in
South Kensington.

The inventive Mr Parkes

Elkington's success was in great part due to the employees and associates who helped to develop different aspects of the company's work at critical points. If George and Henry Elkington did not have the relevant skills and expertise to drive the business forward themselves, then they went out and found those who did, often allowing them considerable freedom in their work. The career of Alexander Parkes (1813-1890) demonstrates this well.

Alexander was born in Birmingham and trained as a decorative metalworker. He came to work for the Elkingtons in the exciting period just as they were moving on from their immersion gilding and plating techniques to their radical new electroplating. Alexander was a natural and prolific researcher, though perhaps not so much of a natural businessman, and his expertise helped build on the Elkingtons' original ideas to produce viable production techniques, key to underpinning the Elkington patent of 1840.

After working on the electroplating process, Alexander went on to refine the associated electrotyping process. He helped to develop this technique to a point where it could capture extremely fine detail, both with works of art and with natural objects. For example, he produced silver-plated spider's webs, one of which was presented to Prince Albert. Interestingly, Parkes' relationship with the company was such that it allowed him to patent some of his inventions. Indeed, his two patents for improved electrotyping methods for use with items such as flowers had to be licensed back by Elkington for their use.

Parkes' strength included looking at potential improvements over all the different stages of the manufacturing process, for example improving the way that moulds could be made from items to be copied. He developed an elastic moulding material, a mixture of India rubber, treacle and glue, which gave a greatly improved mould-making capability. This mould-forming solution enabled the fine detail of complex items to be firstly captured so that remarkably faithful reproductions could be made using the electrotype process.

Inventions poured out of Alexander, not only in the fields of electrochemistry and mould-making, but also in wider areas, such as a method for the de-silvering of lead known as the Parkes process. His process for the industrial-scale electrolytic extraction of copper from its ore, developed during his time at the Elkington Pembrey copper smelting plant in South Wales, was widely used throughout the world until comparatively recently.

Parkesine and Xylonite

During his lifetime, Alexander Parkes accumulated a remarkable total of sixty-six patents. Many of these were directly connected with electroplating, but it is his invention of the world's first plastic in particular which earned him a blue plaque on the small portion of the façade of the Newhall Street factory which still stands.

By the 1850s, the Elkington factories had moved into the large-scale production of

▲ Alexander Parkes. Portrait painted from a pencil drawing by Abraham Wivell.

▶ Xylonite napkin rings. Alexander Parkes named the world's first plastic 'Parkesine'. It was later renamed 'Xylonite'.

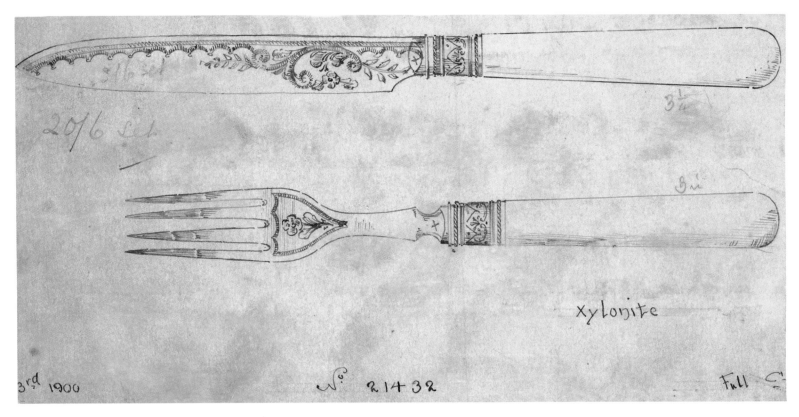

2016 Set

3rd 1900   № 21432   Full

Xylonite

▲ Design number 21432 from the Elkington
pattern books for a fish knife and fork. Xylonite
is specified as the material for the handles.
This new material would have been a cheaper
alternative to the 'African Ivory' for which it
was a substitute.

▶ Fish knives to a similar
pattern to the design above.
The handles have the
appearance of ivory, but are
probably of Xylonite.

◀ Detail from the blade
of the fish knives shown
opposite.

affordable flatware, making items such as knives, forks and spoons. Handles for these came in a choice of materials which might include bone, ivory, horn or tortoiseshell, but these materials could be difficult to source and were not ideal for use in large-scale manufacturing. Around 1852, Parkes left Elkington's employment to work on alternative materials for these items.

Alexander's work culminated in his invention of Parkesine, an early form of celluloid produced by the extraction of cellulose from wood pulp, first patented in 1856. Parkesine was awarded a medal at the International Exhibition of 1862 and in 1866 Parkes, with business partner Daniel Spill, set up a factory on Hackney Marshes in London to produce the new material at scale. Unfortunately, the plastic polymer proved to be fragile and cracked easily, making it difficult to work. The extraction process used alcohol and its highly flammable nature caused a number of factory fires. After a couple of troublesome years, the partnership was would up in 1868.

Daniel Spill managed to continue the business with new partners, eventually finding some success. He renamed the plastic 'Xylonite' and the company moved from Homerton in East London to Brantham in Suffolk, where production continued into the twentieth century. Household items made from Xylonite included brushes, combs and other vanity products, as well as handles for flatware, some of which were sold to Elkington. The factory has now closed and the site is now home to the local Tesco supermarket.

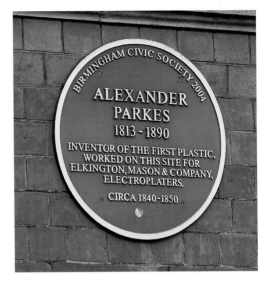

▲ Alexander Parkes is commemorated on the surviving portion of the frontage of the Elkington Newhall Street factory.

▶ Lidded jug (1884, pattern 16587) and a cruet set (1872, pattern 14244) designed by Christopher Dresser, photographed on the Elkington factory site.

5: Design & Industry

The pace of change brought on by the innovation and industry of early Victorian Birmingham was frenetic. The infrastructure of the town was in danger of being overwhelmed, but local champions such as Joseph Chamberlain took measures including building schools, baths and free libraries, clearing slums, and improving the town's sewage system and water supplies, which would ensure it could cope. The firm of Elkington was thriving and by the 1850s even their old competitors in the Sheffield plating business were taking out licences from them to move over to electroplating.

Family life

Alongside the excitement of work, there was also plenty going on at home. George Elkington married Mary Auster Balleney (1804-1858) in 1825 and they had seven surviving children. The families settled in the Selly Oak and Northfield suburbs of Birmingham.

George and his family lived at a fine villa, Woodbrooke, originally built for Josiah Mason and his wife Anne around 1830 as the centrepiece of their 70-acre country estate. The building has since been extended, but the original part of the house contains an impressive wrought iron staircase and tiled floor. The gardens feature a lake, probably landscaped from a quarry from which building materials for the house had been extracted. George purchased Woodbrooke from Mason in 1839, suggesting that the two industrialists knew each other well before Mason became a partner in Elkington in 1842.

▶ Woodbrooke in Selly Oak, originally built for Josiah Mason and later the home of George Elkington.

◀ ▼ The boathouse on the lake at Woodbrooke (left) and the staircase and tiled floor in the hall (below).

The 1841 census records George and Mary as living at Woodbrooke with their family and three servants. After George died in 1865 his son Frederick continued to live at Woodbrooke.

In 1881, the house was sold to the chocolate maker George Cadbury, who lived there until 1894. In 1903, Cadbury gifted Woodbrooke as home to a Quaker learning centre which would 'foster a vital Friends' ministry'. Today this remains an important centre for Quaker studies, but the bed and breakfast accommodation can be booked by anyone who wishes to experience the tranquillity of the house and remaining ten acres of grounds.

George was appointed governor of King Edward's Grammar School and in 1856 became a Borough Magistrate. His first wife died in 1858 and in 1860 he remarried to Margaret Morgan Jones. George Richards Elkington himself died at Pool Park in Denbighshire, North Wales in September 1865.

George and his two wives are remembered in two stained glass panels in St Mary's in Selly Oak, a church for which George had himself donated a substantial part of the building costs. The panels were produced by the Jewellery Quarter firm of John Hardman & Co., whose founder we have already met as one of the partners in the Newhall Street plating works of the 1830s. Hardman had their main manufactory on Newhall Hill and also had a long association with the architect and designer A.W.N. Pugin.

Henry Elkington married Emma Spragget, a cousin. He died in 1852, aged just 41, while living at Summer Hill Terrace in the Jewellery Quarter. He had no surviving children.

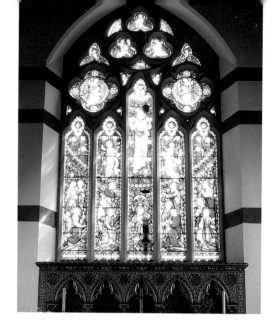

▲ East window, St Mary's Church, Selly Oak (Hardman & Co.). Depicting 'The Ascension', this window commemorates Mary Auster Elkington, George's first wife.

◄ St Mary's Church, Selly Oak

▶ Stained glass window, St Mary's Church, Selly Oak (Hardman & Co.) depicting The Good Samaritan. Erected in the memory of George Richards Elkington by his fellow parishioners in April 1866.

Approaches to design

Elkington's early success owed much to the importance the company placed on design. While this was primarily focussed on the higher end 'Art-Manufactures' produced by Henry, it also had benefits for the everyday items which made up the bulk of the firm's business – both in terms of design quality and in attracting publicity which would drive up sales. In this Elkington can be seen as a shining example of the collaboration between art and industry so strongly promoted by Prince Albert and the Great Exhibition of 1851.

In order to keep on coming up with fresh items to market, the firm required design input in quantity, and they took several different approaches to acquiring it. Sometimes they worked with contemporary designers and artists. As early as 1840, George Elkington came to an agreement with the Birmingham-born silversmith Benjamin Smith III (1793-1850) for Smith to design items for Elkington and market them in his London showrooms. They also reproduced works by established British sculptors such as James Sherwood Westmacott (1823-1900) and John Evan Thomas (1810-1873).

Another approach was to obtain casts of classical works which they could either mould faithful copies from or use as inspiration for their own designs. For the acquisition of these they employed agents on the continent, first Benjamin Schlick (1796-1872) and later Dr. Emil Braun (1809-1856), who also obtained designs from contemporary artists living in Rome, then a centre of the art world.

Elkington also developed their own in-house team of designers and modellers. One of the first members of this was Birmingham born designer George Clark Stanton (1832-1894). After attending King Edwards Grammar School, at the same time as the artist Edward Burne-Jones, Stanton took up a seven-year apprenticeship with Elkington which included studying silversmithing at the Birmingham School of Art. One of his designs was for a small circular table for Prince Albert's display at the Great Exhibition, on which was placed an electrotype of the Rosewater Basin. Today this table can be seen at Osborne House on the Isle-of-Wight.

Stanton had worked mainly with Henry Elkington, and after the latter's, death, in 1854 he embarked on a trip to study Renaissance sculpture and metalwork in Italy. There he met his Scottish wife to be and so Elkington's protégé was lost to Edinburgh, where he worked on major public art pieces such as the Scott Monument.

A significant number of those who were employed in the artistic side of the business originally came, like Leonard Morel-Ladeuil the designer of the Milton Shield (see page 60), from France.

The extraordinary range and quantity of design which Elkington generated can be seen in the remarkable set of pattern books which are held by The Library of Birmingham and the Victoria and Albert Museum. At some point Elkington also acquired another rich source of design material: the pattern books which had belonged to several of Matthew Boulton's

▶ ▼ Page and spine from the Elkington pattern books held by The Library of Birmingham.

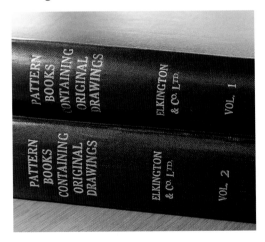

▲ ▶ Sardine tin (1865). Sardines were very popular in Victorian times, often served with a soup course or as part of a high tea. Cornwall was a major centre for the sardine fishing and canning industry. Serving the delicacy at a fashionable table would ideally include the use of special sardine tins and of course a special fork (see overleaf).

◀ Design for a sardine tin from the Elkington pattern books in The Library of Birmingham. This is similar to the example illustrated, but lacks the wide rim above the feet.

firms. These books were cut up and rearranged by Elkington into eight volumes which are today also kept in the Library of Birmingham.

Sadly, Henry Elkington died young in 1852, just as his 'Art-Manufactures' were taking off. George's son Frederic Elkington (1826-1905) took over from Henry, supported by Charles Grant (1801-1883) as chief artist.

Designing for the market

The long-term success of Elkington as a major producer of silver-plated items depended on their ability to update established designs to ensure they fitted with contemporary fashion – an approach which can be traced back to the Richards family jewellery business where George Elkington cut his teeth. Much of Elkington's early work was in the 'organic naturalism' style for which electroplating was ideally suited, being able to reproduce intricate detail which Sheffield plate could not. In the years following the Great Exhibition of 1851, they continued to produce work in this style, but also followed the winds of change as taste started to shift towards a simpler aesthetic. From teapots to sugar sifters, as fashions changed established products were given makeovers to prolong their appeal.

Elkington was particularly successful at identifying and serving newly emerging markets. From the middle of the Victorian era, the advent of mass transport in the form of ocean liners and trains, together with the growth of the hotel and catering industry, were increasingly significant markets for mass-produced silver plate.

The company became adept at customising their products, both for individual clients and for the growing corporate market. From very short production runs of standard lines with personalised family crests, to high volume orders for large shipping lines and hotels, this added value to their production. Some of the most collectable Elkington items today have the insignia of famous brands. For example, items with the mark of the White Star Line, the owners of the Titanic, can command a premium – some Elkington products were even recovered from that most famous of shipwrecks.

Also important for Elkington was their ability to introduce new types of product and market these as the 'must have' items of the day. The marketing department had the job of ensuring that the public saw product lines such as sardine tins, crumb scoops or pickle forks as essential for correct dining etiquette – especially coming up to Christmas.

The ability of Elkington to remain a significant presence into the middle of the twentieth century was in large part due to continuing to update their products for the developing market. Even in the 1950s, wedding present lists would include canteens of Elkington silver-plated flatware, and no christening would be complete without a set of apostle spoons and a child's cutlery set.

The Elkington approach of employing artistic designers of merit was another key to their success. In the later 1800s there was no designer more influential than Christopher Dresser.

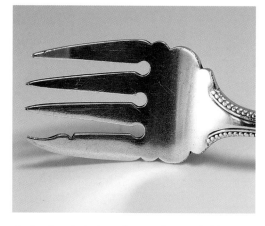

▲ Sardine fork. Dated 1884, but probably designed in the 1860s. Perfect for use with the sardine tin on the previous page.

▶ ▼ Centre-table butter dish (1920, pattern 32112). This example features the Cunard Steamship Co. logo both on the side and dish itself. Underneath the butter tray is a water reservoir which helped to keep the butter cool.

▲ Tea Strainer (1960, pattern 30284). Produced for Rackham's department store in Birmingham and featuring their logo.

◀ Detail of the Grand Hotel mark

▶ Coffee pot (1957, pattern 38799), shown with a teapot (1947, 36411) marked for Birmingham's Grand Hotel, just a short walk from the Newhall Street factory and shown in the background.

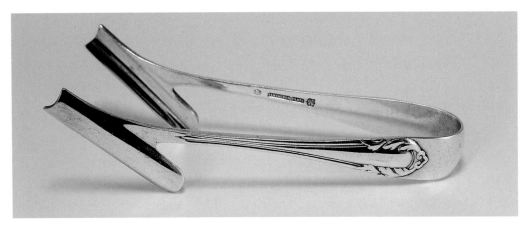

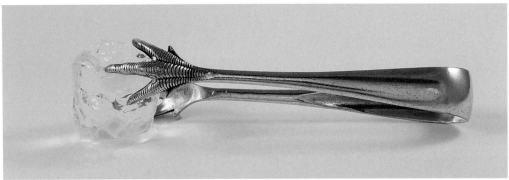

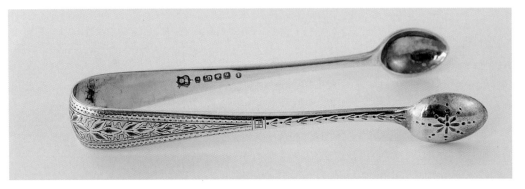

Specialist tableware – Victorian and Edwardian dining etiquette required an ever-growing range of specialist cutlery, providing an ideal market for Elkington.

▲ Spork (1867): This spoon and fork one-piece is also known as a 'party fork'.

▶ Asparagus tongs (1913): Serving asparagus was a serious business. These are angled and designed for a strong spring-like action.

▼ Ice tongs (1910). This example was produced for the Union Castle Line which specialised in services to Africa.

◀ Bone marrow scoop (1880). Beef bone marrow eaten straight from the cooked bone was a particular delicacy. This example is double-ended to deal with large and small bones alike.

◀ Sugar tongs (1894)

▶ Stilton cheese scoop (1869). Stilton and a glass of port were a traditional end to a Victorian meal. The tray is dated 1850.

Christopher Dresser and his influence

Of all those involved in designing Elkington products, Christopher Dresser (1834-1904) is now the most revered, and he designed some of the most sought after of Elkington's wares. Dresser was born in Glasgow and aged just thirteen went to train at the Government School of Design at Somerset House in London, predecessor of the Royal College of Art. By his early twenties he was lecturing there. Dresser epitomised the ideology of applying art and science to industry, as expounded by Henry Cole's 'South Kensington system'.

Today, Dresser is considered a pioneer of modern design and sometimes called the 'father of industrial design'. His radical works seem way ahead of their time and even today one might easily assume that his clean-cut designs were products of 1960s rather than the 1880s.

Dresser's 1870 book *Principles of Victorian Decorative Design* brought together essays originally published in the *Technical Educator* magazine. In his essay on silverware, Dresser emphasised that objects should be designed to 'perfectly serve the end for which they have been formed'. He pointed to the high value of gold and silver as raw materials and advocated using just enough material for functional integrity but avoiding over-indulgent design which might result in expensive and heavy items. A good example of Dresser's approach is his discussion on the positioning of teapot handles and spouts, in which he suggested that these should be aligned to maximise balanced pouring, taking into account

▶ James Dixon & Sons of Sheffield, teapot (c.1880). Christopher Dresser's teapot designs were described as 'English-Japanese' in Dixon's catalogues. The angularity and mix of shapes shows his progressive designs as a forerunner to twentieth century design. These designs, entered in his pattern books on 25 November 1880, are considered to be some of Dresser's most original.

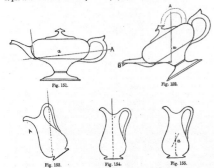

◀ A discussion of teapots and jugs from Dresser's *Principles of Victorian Decorative Design*, the images helping to illustrate the best positioning for handles and spouts.

140   PRINCIPLES OF VICTORIAN DECORATIVE DESIGN.

pots. Now if the part which is grasped is to the right or left of a right line passing through the centre of gravity of any vessel, there is leverage acting to the disadvantage of the person desiring to pour from that vessel, and this leverage increases just as the point held is removed from the central line spoken of.

Fig. 151 would pour when in the position shown in Fig. 152, but see how far the hand that holds it would be to the right of the centre of gravity (*a*), which distance is of great disadvantage, as it causes the vessel to appear much heavier than it actually is, and requires a much greater expenditure of force in order that the tea-pot be put to its use than is necessary were it properly formed.

The law governing the application of handle and spout to vessels is this, and the same principle applies whether the vessel be formed of metal, glass, or earthenware :—Find the centre of gravity of the vessel, which can easily be done by letting a vertical line drop over it when placed in two different positions, as in Figs. 153, 154, and where the two vertical lines intersect, as in *a* in Fig. 155, is the centre of gravity. The position of the handle being fixed on, draw a line through the centre of the handle, and continue it through the centre of gravity of the vessel. The spout must now be at right angles to this line. If this be the case the vessel will pour freely while the handle is just hung upon the thumb or finger of the person desiring to pour from it, as may be seen from Figs. 156, 157, in which the straight line A,

SPOUTS AND HANDLES.   141

passing through the centre of gravity *a*, is at right angles, as it should be, with the straight line passing through the spout.

This law, if obeyed, will always enable liquid to be poured from a vessel without its appearing heavier than it actually is, but it will be seen that the shape of the vessel must be considered so that the spout and handle can bear this relation to each other, as in Figs. 156, 157, 158, 159, and 160. Some shapes will not admit of it, so they must be avoided, as may be seen by examining Figs. 151 and 152, which show a tea-pot of faulty shape in this respect.

A consideration of this law shows that the handles of jugs—those formed of silver, of glass, and of earthenware alike—are usually placed too high; but in this respect things are much better than they were a few years back. Now we somewhat frequently see a jug with the handle in the right place, while some years back we never did. Silver jugs are now the most generally faulty in this respect, and such mistakes as the wrong placing of the handle or spout of a vessel result only from ignorance, for no man knowing the law would violate it. Fig. 161 shows a

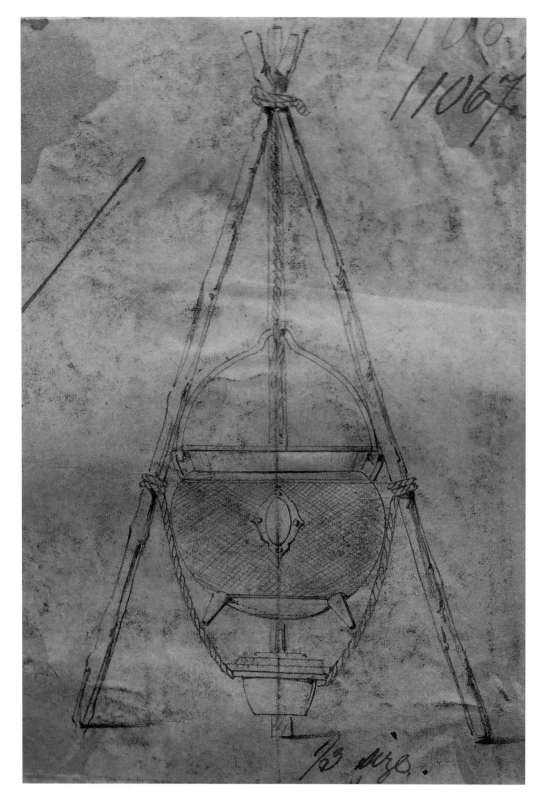

▶ ▲ Cauldron (1884) shown right with lid, burner and stand and above with hot toddy ladle (1885). If not designed by Christopher Dresser then clearly inspired by his work.

◀ Drawing of the cauldron from the Elkington pattern books

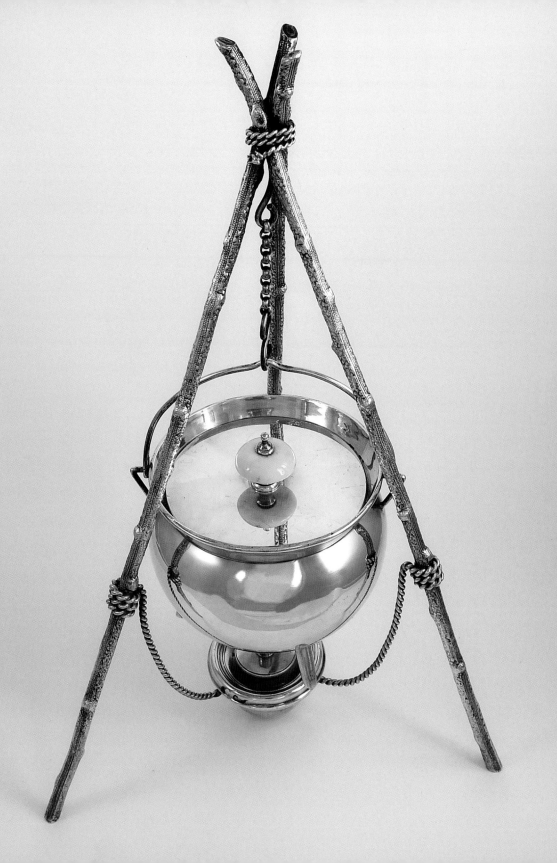

the vessel's centre of gravity. His examples (see page 86) show a design where the centre of gravity is wrong (Fig. 151-5) in comparison to a teapot (Fig. 151-2) looking remarkably similar to an Elkington product of the day. Regarding jugs (Fig. 153-50), Dresser notes that handles were 'usually placed too high' but that now 'we somewhat frequently see a jug with the handle in the right place, while some years back we never did'.

Unlike Dresser's decorative designs for ceramics and glass, where his botanical influences are clear, Dresser's designs in metal were generally clean-cut and abstract. His ideas were often in contrast to the ideals of the Arts & Crafts movement, as expounded by William Morris and John Ruskin. Indeed, Ruskin was a vehement critic of Cole's South Kensington system and its application to manufacturing. However, the Arts and Crafts movement's emphasis on traditional production techniques had no place for Dresser. He saw new industrial processes not as threats to craftsmanship but as opportunities which would allow new designs to be produced – and to be produced economically and in volume so that many more people could afford to purchase them.

Dresser had praised Elkington's techniques and designs as early as 1862. He is thought to have provided design input from the mid-1860s and his influences can certainly be seen in Elkington pattern books from 1866.

▶ Cruet set (1897, pattern 14244). An imaginative Christopher Dresser design integrating the salt with egg-shaped pepper and mustard pots. This design was also produced in solid silver by Thomas Bradbury & Sons.

▼ Claret or water Jug (1884, pattern 16587). Designed by Christopher Dresser in the 'aesthetic' style. Features a double-hinged lid, seen in a number of Dresser's designs, which allowed liquid to be poured while the main lid remained closed.

Dresser challenged the elaborate naturalism epitomised by much of the work which had been displayed at the Great Exhibition of 1851. He expounded a simplicity and honesty in design. The metal items he designed are some of his most innovative, sometimes even including exposed structural elements such as rivets and hinges. Dresser became increasingly influenced by Japanese design, especially after, on his way home from the World Exhibition in Philadelphia in 1876, he made a four-month visit to Japan, funded by a London importer and Tiffany's of New York. His use of rectilinear shapes and Japanese influence is well demonstrated in the quirky teapots he designed for James Dixon and Sons of Sheffield in the 1880s (see page 85). Japanese influence can be seen in the teapot handle, but did not extend to detail in the finishing – the overall appearance seems remarkably contemporary today.

Dresser's influence was profound, helping to move Victorian manufacturers away from the elaborate naturalism of the mid 1800s. His output was also prolific and his designs were used by perhaps fifty manufacturers, not only in metalwork but also in textiles, carpets, ceramics, glass and furniture.

▲ Knife Sharpener (c1910). A simple and practical, yet elegant design in the spirit of Dresser.

▶ A selection of Elkington toast racks photographed beside the pool at Woodbrooke.

6: Decline and Legacy

After George Elkington died in 1865, his five sons – Frederick, James, Alfred, Howard and Hyla – continued the family business. In 1887, the firm registered as a Limited Company. The new managing director of Elkington & Co. Ltd. was Thomas Henry Rollason (1832-1908) who was the nephew of Dr John Wright's widow and had joined Elkington in 1848. Among the other directors were George's son Frederick Elkington and his sons Herbert Frederick Elkington and Gerard Bartlett Elkington, as well as Hyla Garrett Elkington, son of Hyla Elkington.

Competition and a changing market

By the middle of the twentieth century, the design of household items was changing under the influence of new styles and new materials, contributing to a move away from the sort of silverware which Elkington produced. However, the decline of the firm had roots well before that, with increased competition from around the world, together with a lack of long-term investment in new production techniques.

An early competitor from the New World was the Gorham Manufacturing Company of Rhode Island. In 1852, John Gorham, son of the company's founder, visited Elkington & Co. as part of a fact-finding tour which also took in factories in Sheffield, London and Paris. Upon his return, Gorham pronounced that there was nothing to fear from English or European competition, commenting that processes which were being done by hand in Europe were done by machinery in his American factories. If this was an early warning sign it was not heeded. Nearly fifty years later, in 1896, British designer Charles Ashbee visited Gorham's factory and was impressed, writing that in England there was neither the 'capital nor the means nor the wits to put in the newest American machinery, nor the

▶ Apostle Spoons (1858). This type of spoon has been a popular baptismal present since Tudor times. These particular spoons, photographed in St Philip's churchyard, feature the typical barley twist stem seen on many of Elkington's flatware products.

◀ St Philip's Church (now Cathedral), Birmingham was where the Elkingtons came to baptise their children.

Child's spoon and fork in presentation case (1958). A popular christening present, and typical of the sort of items Elkington were producing towards the end.

brains, even if it were possible to do so, to accept and work in with the Arts and Crafts movement.' The Gorham chief designer told Ashbee that their skilled labour came mainly from England and said of Elkington that 'the whole thing is dead!'

The days of Elkington's prestigious arrangement to copy items for the V&A were also numbered. The contractual basis for this had always been somewhat loose. In theory, Elkington were only allowed to make copies for sale to other museums or the public if the contract with the object's owner allowed. But while those contracts were between the owner and the Museum, it was Elkington who stored the 'type patterns' from which copies could be made and the museum had no proper system to check how these were used. It is clear that Elkington were not always scrupulous in observing these rules and sold copies which they should not have done. In 1915, there was a final breakdown in trust between the firm and the museum who ended the relationship, asking for the pattern types to be returned to them (this was done, although the parcels were only opened recently by Museum staff).

Despite this setback and the growing commercial pressures, Elkington continued to be a major manufacturer into the middle of the twentieth century but in 1943, when the company was heavily involved in war work, the firm was taken over by Mercury Securities. In 1949 Elkington re-entered the copper-refining field and acquired the site of an old leather tanning factory on Goscote Lane in Walsall. The silver plating part of the business moved to this new location. In 1955, Mercury Securities disposed of Elkington to the Birmingham and Greenwich based Delta Metals Group and the Newhall Street and Brearley Street factories were closed. Catalogues from this era are preserved in Walsall Library Archive which features the new plating line supplied by W. Canning and Co. of

Cover and selected pages from a 1950s Elkington catalogue

► Plating baths in a photograph from an Elkington catalogue of the 1950s. The process seems little changed from the illustration on page 38 from c.1857.

► The new automated plating line installed at the Goscote Lane works, from an Elkington catalogue of the 1950s

Great Hampton Street in the Jewellery Quarter, a firm founded in 1785 who had been developing electroplating equipment for many years.

By the 1960s, stainless steel was becoming the dominant material used in flatware production. It overcame the major downside of silver plate as it greatly reduced the need for cleaning to remove tarnishing. This, together with the rise of items made out of new types of plastic, gradually saw silver-plated items being sent to live a new life in the attic. In 1971 Elkington, along with a number of other well-known silverware firms, were amalgamated into what is today British Silverware. This company continues to produce and market products under the Elkington brand, although now from premises on banks of the River Don in Sheffield.

The Elkington site today

The modern Jewellery Quarter is a vibrant mix. Traditional industries are still to be found, alongside old industrial premises converted for commercial and residential use. But the redevelopment of the Elkington's Newhall Street factory site has been a relatively protracted process.

In 1951, after the closure of the factory, part of its site found a new use as home to the Birmingham Museum of Science and Industry. However, this closed in 1997 and in 1999 the museum's exhibits were moved to what is now Thinktank, Birmingham Science Museum. Other items were put into storage at the Museum Collection Centre in Nechells. Redevelopment work started soon after that, but has only been completed with the opening of Newhall Square in 2020.

▶ Islington Gates Footbridge over the Birmingham & Fazeley Canal where it passes through the site of the Elkington factory. The design of some of the new flats seen in the background has echoes of that of the demolished factory.

◀ ▼ The surviving part of the Elkington factory façade on Newhall Street. The blue plaque commemorating George Elkington (below) is on the small white building. The other plaque is to Alexander Parkes.

◄ Crowds come out to see the locomotive City of Birmingham being moved after the closure of the Museum of Science and Industry in 1999.

A few parts of the old factory remain, including a section of the Newhall Street façade which houses a blue plaque marking the Elkington factory site and another remembering Alexander Parkes. The old canal arm known as Miss Colmore's Canal, which ran right through the factory, has been commemorated by a water feature along part of its line. This was later known as the Whitmore Canal, after iron founder William Whitmore (1748-1819). The old warehouse alongside was probably built in the mid-1800s on what had been the site of Whitmore's foundry, where he manufactured rolling and flatting mills and weighing machines for barges and wagons. The foundry also supplied metalwork for the Stratford Canal.

Today there are several new developments on the Elkington site. Earlier phases included a hotel and retail premises, while the final phases, known as The Whitmore Collection and Newhall Square included the development of 220 dwellings. These properties are rented on terms of six months to five years and residents have access to communal facilities such as lounges and a gym. Backed by Legal & General, this represents an interesting move into the city centre rental market by a major investor.

▶ The Whitmore Warehouse in 2021 after the redevelopment of the Elkington site. The water feature in the foreground marks the route of the Whitmore Canal (formerly Miss Colmore's Canal).

◄ Lock on the Birmingham & Fazeley Canal by the entrance to the tunnel which takes the waterway under Newhall Street and on to the north east of the city.

Electroplating today

Today, electroplating is still widely used in a variety of modern industries central to life all around us. As well as coating surfaces to enhance their appearance, electroplating techniques have a variety of other applications, for example depositing layers of oxide to improve resistance to corrosion, or silver chloride to increase the conductivity of specialist electrodes, while the technique of 'electropolishing' reverses the process so that a thin layer of material is removed from an object, leaving it cleaner. Furthermore, techniques rooted in Elkington's electrotyping and electroplating processes are used in the most advanced modern technologies, from the production of microprocessors to electron microscopy.

It is exciting to find that today, within a short walk from George Elkington's family home in St Paul's Square, electroplating techniques are still in use on a large scale by long-established firms. One such company is J. Hudson of Barr Street, on the edge of the Jewellery Quarter. Founded in the 1870s, they export their 'ACME' whistles around the world, where they are used by referees at sporting events or by platform staff at railway stations – and of course you can hear them in school playgrounds up and down the country. Their electrolysis room has mini-jig dipping baths to help with the finishing of their range of brass whistles. They have different baths for nickel, silver and gold electroplating, into which the whistles are dipped while suspended on a cathode rail.

Even closer to Newhall Street and St Paul's Square is the firm of E.C. Williams Ltd who have operated from Spencer Street since they started to offer nickel silver electroplating services to Jewellery Quarter firms in 1921. They have extended and modernised their factory and equipment several times since. During World War II, the company adapted to help the war effort, producing functional anti-corrosion finishes. After the war, with ornamental plating in decline but the Midlands car industry growing, this new area of expertise became especially important and the company is now a key part of the automotive component supply chain.

E.C. Williams' state of the art barrel plating production equipment allows high throughput and a single worker can process up to 10 tons of components a week. The parts are first prepared in a pre-plating processes, before being arranged in contact with each other so that they form a cathode in a non-conductive barrel, which is lowered through first cleaning and then electrolytic solutions. For larger components, an individual jig dipping process can be used.

The company also electroplates numerous products for the electrical and electromechanical industries in copper, which is also used as a base coat to enhance the adhesion of tin, silver and nickel plating. From the 1990s, the company has also been involved in zinc-nickel alloy plating – this offers an environmentally friendly alternative to cadmium for components for the automotive, aerospace and off-shore industries where excellent resistance to salt water spray is required. With the growth in electric vehicle

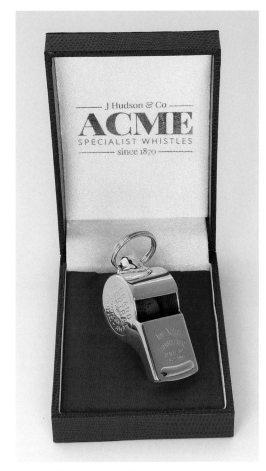

▲ A gold-plated ACME Thunderer whistle in presentation case

▶ The electroplating baths at whistle makers J. Hudson

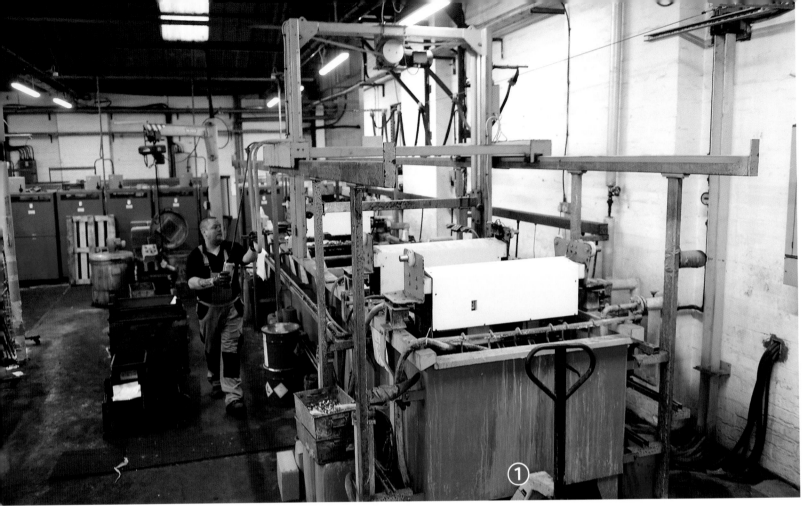

Copper plating using the barrel process

1. Overview of one of the smaller barrel plating lines at E. C. Williams

2. The metal brake components as they arrive from the customer, ready to be placed in the barrel

3. Copper anode pellets are added to the electrolyte solution in the tanks

4. The barrel is moved between tanks

5. The barrel is opened to reveal the copper plated components

6. The components are finished before being sent back to the customer

▲ ▶ A collection of Elkington ware reflected in the pool in front of the Library of Birmingham (pictured above).

production, tin-plated components which offer high, durable conductivity are a current growth area for the company.

So, over 180 years since their original development by two driven young men in St Paul's Square and Newhall Street, we can still find modern-day adaptations of the Elkingtons' processes in use just a few minutes' walk away from where it all started.

The 'Birmingham way'

This fast-moving story of highly motivated people driving new innovations forward is one which epitomises what we might call the 'Birmingham way'. This approach had its roots in the town long before the Elkingtons arrived in St Paul's Square and had been perfected by the entrepreneurs of the Georgian age. The elements of the 'Birmingham way' went far beyond simply concentrating on financial return – they included the application of the latest inventions and discoveries to the needs of the real world; the bringing together of people with the right range of skills, allowing them freedom to develop their ideas; an emphasis on good design, high quality and keeping up with fashion; the use of patents and lobbying and to protect business; and an emphasis on marketing which included cultivating friends in high places. These were elements which George and Henry Elkington were able to apply to their business with such remarkable success.

▲ The Birmingham coat of arms encapsulates the Birmingham way. The figures represent art (left) and industry (right) and the motto is 'Forward'.

◀ Relief panel depicting electroplating (Samuel Lynn, 1869). One of four panels celebrating Birmingham industry in the entrance of the National and Provincial Bank, Bennett's Hill, (now the Lost and Found pub). The other panels represent metalworking, gun making and glass blowing.

▶ Elkington teapot, milk jug and coffee pot reflected in the fountains of Centenary Square, Birmingham.

Appendices

Appendix 1:

Basics of electroplating and electroforming

Electroplating

In its simplest form, electroplating uses the process of electrodeposition to add a thin coating of metal to a solid substrate which is acting as the cathode (negative electrode) of an electrical cell. The anode (positive electrode) is made of the metal which will form the coating. Between these is a conductive salt solution, known as the electrolyte, which includes dissolved positive ions (cations) of the metal which will form the coating. The current is produced by a DC electrical source such as a battery which causes electrons to move from the anode to the cathode. At the cathode, the positive metal ions are reduced by the addition of electrons, depositing, atom by atom, a layer of pure metal.

In the example shown, the electrolyte for silver plating could be silver nitrate, with potassium cyanide as a major bath constituent. The silver (Ag) in solution is dissociated into Ag+ cations. At the cathode, the Ag+ is reduced to metallic silver by gaining an electron and is deposited on the cathode surface – in this case a spoon. The anode is made of solid silver and here the opposite reaction sees it dissolved as the metal moves into the solution to become an Ag+ cation – so replacing the silver that has been deposited at the cathode. The rate at which the anode dissolves equals the plating rate of the cathode so the overall result is the controlled transfer of metal from the anode to the cathode.

The ability of a plating bath to cover an object uniformly is called its 'throwing power' – the better the throwing power the more uniform the coating. Traditionally, electrolytes include cyanides to improve conductivity and facilitate anode corrosion, although today cyanide-free processes are also available. Non-metal chemicals such as carbonates and phosphates might also be added to increase conductivity.

The anode can also be made of a material that is resistant to electrochemical oxidation, such as lead or carbon. In this case the anode is not dissolved but oxygen, hydrogen peroxide, or some other by-products are produced at the anode instead. Ions of the metal which is being used for plating must then be manually replenished in the bath as they are lost out of the solution.

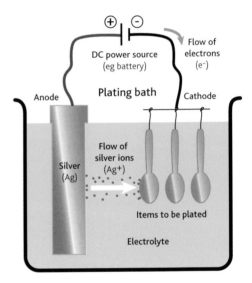

▲ The electroplating process

When plating is not desired on certain areas of the substrate, 'stop-offs' can be applied to prevent the liquid in the bath from coming in contact with the substrate. Typical materials for stop-offs include tape, foil, lacquers, and waxes.

Multi-ion electroplating

Usually, a plated coating is formed of just a single metallic element, not an alloy of different metals. Some alloys, such as brass (copper and zinc) and solder (tin and lead), can be electrodeposited, although technically the result is a mixture rather than a true alloy. However, where the properties of a true alloy are required, a plated coating of mixed metals can be heat treated afterwards so that they combine to form a true alloy

Electroforming

This technique, known in Elkington's day as electrotyping, uses the same process of electrodeposition that is used in electroplating, but it is continued for longer to lay down a much greater thickness of metal. A mould is first made from an item to be copied. Then, the surface of the mould is coated with a material such as lead paint to make it conductive. After this, the mould is placed in an electrolyte bath to form the cathode in a circuit. When the current is switched on, metal ions come out of the solution and adhere to the surface of the mould so that a new piece is gradually produced.

Many of the electrotypes which Elkington produced were made in sections which then had to be assembled to make the complete piece before being finished by electrotyping with silver, gold, or both.

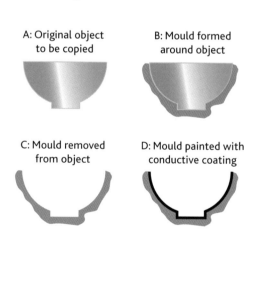

A: Original object to be copied

B: Mould formed around object

C: Mould removed from object

D: Mould painted with conductive coating

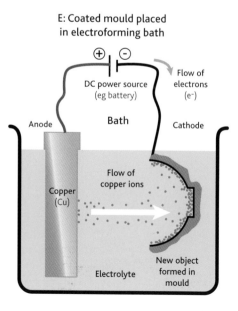

E: Coated mould placed in electroforming bath

⊕ ⊖

DC power source (eg battery)

Flow of electrons (e⁻)

Anode

Bath

Cathode

Copper (Cu)

Flow of copper ions

Electrolyte

New object formed in mould

◀ The electroforming process

Appendix 2:

Elkington trade marks

The precious metal trade in Birmingham received a major boost in 1773 when a group of industrialists, including Matthew Boulton, persuaded Parliament to agree to the establishment of the Birmingham Assay Office where the testing and 'hallmarking' of silver and gold items could be done locally. The Birmingham hallmark is an anchor and the Assay Office was, until 2015, located directly opposite the Elkington Newhall Street works.

While there was no legal obligation to test and mark silver-plated items, they often have 'trade marks' that look like hallmarks, a suggestion of quality if not a guarantee. Elkington developed their own system for marking and dating their products. This makes it much easier today to check the origins of items on the market. The advantages of this can be seen when we make a comparison with the japanning industry, where the lack of even a maker's mark means that it is usually impossible to distinguish with any certainty the output of, for example, that of John Baskerville's factories from his competitors.

Elkington understood the increasing importance of a clear provenance to distinguish their products from the poor quality 'brummagem ware' and to build what today we would call a 'brand identity'. They used their own punches to add trade marks to their electroplate. From 1840, their manufacturer's mark was 'E&Co' in a shield with a crown above. This mark lasted until 1896 when the Sheffield Assay Office, established at the same time as the Birmingham office, threatened electroplate manufacturers with legal action over the use of the crown as it mimicked the Sheffield hallmark. This was clearly targeted at Elkington and by 1898 the crown element disappeared from Elkington products. The Sheffield office had a point and it is perhaps surprising they took so long to take action. It was certainly no accident that the trade marks on Elkington's plated items looked similar to the hallmarks used on silver.

From 1841, a year number (1-8) was added to the trade mark. From 1849 this was changed to a year letter, starting with the letter 'K' within a diamond and moved on to a new sequence of letters within different shapes each time 'Z' was reached (although not all letters were consistently used across all departments). From 1842, when Josiah Mason became a partner in the company, the letter 'M' was added to become 'E M & Co'; this mark continued to be used on some items even after he ceased to be a partner in 1861. The trade mark and associated year mark were sometimes punched separately, meaning Mason's mark can appear on items date marked well after he left the company. It also suggests Elkington's marking system sometimes recorded year of sale rather than of manufacture.

▲ An example of Elkington assay marks. The 'E & Co' in a shield under a crown was used from 1841 to 1898. Below that is the date letter E for 1867, under which is a gothic letter E for Elkington. Below that a Patent Office registry mark.

▲ This example from 1845 uses the earliest date marking system with the number '5' in a diamond signifying the year. The gothic letter stamps 'E' 'M' '& Co.' stand for Elkington, Mason & Co.

As an early form of intellectual property rights, between 1842 and 1883, a registry mark was used by the British Patent Office for British manufactured goods and was designed to show the date a design was registered and protected. These records are held at the National Records Office in Kew.

For those researching Elkington pieces, more detailed information can be found online.

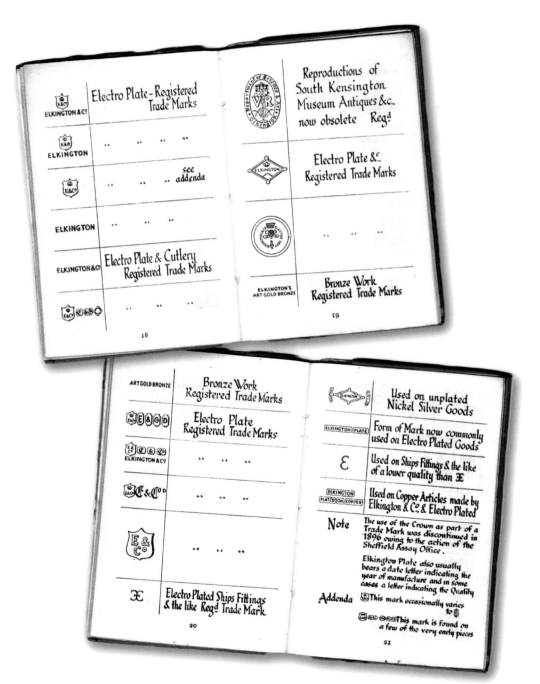

◀ A list published by Elkington in 1923 which shows their various trade marks.

Further reading

William Bennett, *John Baskerville; the Birmingham printer, vols I & II*.
(Birmingham: City of Birmingham School of Printing, 1937)

Shirley Bury, *Victorian Electroplate*
(Country life collector's Guides. Feltham: Hamlyn, 1971)

Christopher Dresser, *Principles of Victorian decorative design*
(London: Cassell, Petter, & Galpin, 1873)

Alistair Grant & Angus Patterson, *The museum and the factory*.
(Lund Humphries in association with V&A publishing, 2018)
An outstanding book looking at the relationship between Elkington and the V&A.
Simply inspirational!

Alistair Grant, *Elkington & Co. and the Art of Electro-Metallurgy, circa 1840-1900*
(PhD thesis, University of Sussex, 2014. Available to download at: sro.sussex.ac.uk)

William Hutton, *An History of Birmingham : To the End of the Year 1780*
(Birmingham: Pearson and Rollason, 1783)
Modern reprints are also available.

Illustration credits

The photography in this book is © Jonathan Berg with the following exceptions:

Barbara Berg: page iv

Henrik Skouby: page v

Birmingham Museums Trust: pages 9, 10, 12, 14, 15, 24, 36, 48 licensed under CC0

Science and Society Picture Library: pages 31, 38, 64, all rights reserved

Neil Hall/EPA: page 59, all rights reserved

Library of Birmingham: photos of Ann Street originally by Robert White Thrupp (1821-1907) (archive references: WK/B11/5949 and WK/B11/5950), page 29; illustration of the Elkington factory from *Cornish's Strangers guide through Birmingham*, page 44.

British Silverware, Sheffield: Pattern books of Elkington held in the archive of the Library of Birmingham (MS 3945/1/1 – 3), pages 75, 76, 86.

Victoria and Albert Museum: endpapers, pages 45, 46, 50, 61, 66

Walsall Central Library and Archives: pages vi, 94, 95

Dr Alistair Grant, University of Sussex: page 111

Bernard Sleigh: Imagined map of Birmingham in 1730, page 16-17. It has not been possible to trace the owner of the intellectual rights to this work (thanks to Chipping Campden History Society for their help in this matter).

About the author

Dr Jonathan Berg is a retired hospital Pathology Director and Honorary Professor of Clinical Biochemistry at the University of Birmingham. He has lived and worked in Birmingham since 1978. As well as his NHS career Jonathan has produced multiple editions of the book *Positively Birmingham* and the tourist guide *Discovering Birmingham*. In the 1990s he ran a photographic library of Birmingham with his wife Barbara. Today Jonathan runs the popular Positively Birmingham Walking Tours with city centre walks throughout the year for local people and visitors alike.

Index